Innovation & Achievement

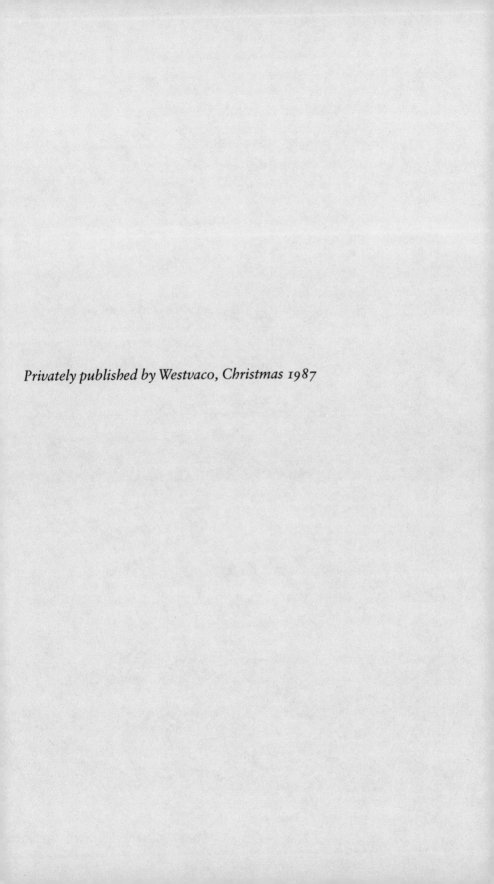

Privately published by Westvaco, Christmas 1987

Eli Whitney

Robert Fulton

C. H. McCormick

Saml. F. B. Morse

Elias Howe Jr

Alexander Graham Bell

Thomas A. Edison.

Orville Wright

Wilbur Wright

Henry Ford

James D. Watson

Jack St Clair Kilby

Robert N Noyce

In praise and recognition of American creativity

Innovation & Achievement

There is a natural aristocracy among men.
The grounds are virtue and talents.
Thomas Jefferson

Westvaco

Foreword

For those of us in Westvaco who have enjoyed over many years the challenge of producing our limited edition series, it always gives us a nice feeling, when visiting our friends and neighbors, to see the distinctive volumes being displayed with pride in the office or on the library shelf in the home. *Innovation & Achievement*, our current selection, represents a significant milestone in the series. This is our thirtieth edition. Substantively, it will occupy a special place in the program for a philosophical reason as well. The volume reflects, in many ways, the spirit of innovation which has been so important as the driving force of Westvaco progress for nearly a century. Moreover, many of the precepts which it demonstrates are being emulated as part of our present strategy for corporate growth.

The original idea for the series, an innovation in its own right as a corporate program, was conceived in 1958. The books have been produced with uninterrupted continuity since then based on one firmly held belief—that the richness of American literature is worthy of being passed along from one generation to the next. In the editions which precede this one, it had become virtually a tradition, in selecting the contents, and by nature of how the volumes were crafted, to pay homage to American men and women of letters.

In this volume, we decided to alter our course, if only slightly. We decided to use our great American literary heritage to enable us to pay homage, in this instance not to a specific American author of note, but rather to the dynamic process which provides America's unique climate for progress – the freedoms, the recognition and rewards, elements which have been fundamental in the economic growth of our nation, its quality of life, and the opportunity which it provides.

We began by asking ourselves a fundamental question: What is it that has truly given America its economic vibrancy and the remarkable standard of living that is so envied throughout the world? In striving to answer this question, it occurred to us that there will be those who will say that our rich natural resources and climate have all combined to nourish the progress of our nation. Yet, we concluded that, although other nations of the world have also been blessed with fine, natural resources, somehow other nations in the world have not risen as consistently to such greatness.

We adopted the point of view that America's great wealth represents a return on the investment of something quite different. America's greatest resource, we concluded, came to our country, with few exceptions, originally from other countries. Yet, it is a resource which is almost always greatly enhanced in value once it reaches our shores. The truth is that America's people have made America great. People from every corner of the earth have come to America to fulfill a dream, and the dream has been fulfilled by a willingness to work, in striving to do better, and by having pride in a job well done.

From our nation's beginning, hard, dedicated work has been in league with life, liberty, and the pursuit of happiness. Rather than rich natural resources, it is this fundamental American quality that long ago became the basic unit of value in America as it had never been in other nations of the world.

Our work on the book also brought to mind another reason for our progress as a nation. One of freedom's great blessings is the wonderful climate it provides for innovation and achievement. Here, wherever Americans work, wherever the stars and stripes fly, a special kind of American, a person willing to expend incredible effort, well beyond the call of ordinary achievement, can stand tall above the crowd and, in doing so, change the course of history to the benefit of all. Certainly it is true that there always seems to be remarkable power in groups of people. But usually the underlying force for extraordinary progress stems from the lonely task of the creative individual. This individual, though not always being the first in the conception of an idea, is the one who stays with the idea until its promise is fulfilled.

Thomas Jefferson appreciated the importance of the creative individual of whom we speak. He realized the importance of providing a fertile climate which fosters high achievement by the individual. He stressed the importance of recognition and praise for those who, through unusual ingenuity, dedication, perseverance, and the taking of personal risk, could make a major difference in the progress of a new nation.

Thomas Jefferson envisioned for the new America a democracy of opportunity out of which might arise what he called "an aristocracy of achievement." Jefferson's aristocracy of achievement is singularly

American. It is not based on title. Nor is it predicated on one's station in life. Its price of admission depends squarely on individual effort. It demands persistence and the pursuit of excellence. And Jefferson was right. The system works.

When a fellow American rises to the occasion through supreme effort to accomplish something worthwhile, surpassing even our greatest expectations, we, too, are there in the winner's circle. And at the moment of victory, there is a feeling of pride throughout the land. There is a sense of a better tomorrow. There is a resilient willingness to keep on trying ourselves.

It is at this wonderful moment, it is at this very eclipse of exceptional effort, and it is at this very pinnacle of personal achievement that we, together as a nation, as Americans, are at our very best.

We were at our very best when Robert Fulton steamed up the Hudson while others scoffed and said it couldn't be done. We were at our very best when Thomas Edison's light burned brightly in his laboratory at Menlo Park. We were at our very best when Wilbur and Orville Wright faced the wind on the dunes at Kitty Hawk. We were at our very best when James Watson in his laboratory reached his moment of triumph, outdistancing others who sought the same prize.

It might be said that wanting to be first on new frontiers of achievement long ago became an American trait. We carry in our blood the genes of pioneers.

Our heritage is one of pressing onward despite the hazards of the unknown. As a people, we are not intimidated by signs that say hazardous journey, instant danger, or safe return doubtful. It is part of our makeup to take risk, meet the challenge, and seek the reward at the end of the rainbow.

Innovation and achievement, together, are America's powerful engine of progress which helps create our quality of life. They give us the economic advantages which we enjoy. They are the reasons that our progress and results are almost unrivaled by the other societies of the world. And, America's record is impressive. Throughout our history, American economic genius has helped produce millions of jobs. In the last decade alone, while job creation in much of the world remained stagnant, twenty-five million new jobs—from the factories to the professions—have been created as a result of American innovation and achievement.

As the author of our Declaration of Independence sought to remind us more than two hundred years ago, innovation and achievement are qualities worth recognizing and praising; qualities worth emphasizing again and again. And that is the purpose of our wanting to recount the legends of innovation and achievement which follow.

The message which they bring to bear has special meaning at a time when our nation seems to be searching for new ways to renew its vigor in the world of international competition. Moreover, the lessons which the chapters communicate so clearly would also seem to provide a renewed sense of purpose for the young people of our nation. Some of our younger friends may feel at times that the golden door of opportunity in America is closed. With respect to opportunity for the new generation, if the book has one clear message, it is simply this: The golden door of opportunity in America has awfully big hinges on it. There is no lock. It is designed to be opened, and opened wide to ever expanding new horizons of opportunity.

We've selected a handful of our fellow Americans to make this point as dramatically as we know how, but the individuals we have selected are simply representative of many, many others who have also proven able to achieve excellence through uncommon effort. They were able to create breakthroughs that changed the nature of our lives for the better, and by this token, they contributed to America's greatness.

To make their mark, they have each traveled a high road of achievement in the pursuit of their dreams. We invite you to be there with them at the ultimate, splendid moment of triumph.

Contents

4

83 Samuel F. B. Morse, 1835

I was about to give up, but then
Gale showed me how to wind the bar of iron.
I opened and closed the circuit.
The apparatus showed some response.

5

109 Elias Howe, Jr., 1845

They asked me if my machine
could compete in a demonstration
with five of their best seamstresses.
It did and the work was declared to be superior.

6

125 Alexander Graham Bell, 1875

Watson, what did you do then?
Don't change anything. Let me see!

7

149 Thomas A. Edison, 1879

The lamp continued to burn. . . .
None of us could go to bed.
We sat and just watched it
with anxiety growing into elation.
It lasted about forty-five hours.

8

177 The Wright Brothers, 1903

We pushed back the doors
and looked outside over the dunes.
It was clearly hopeless to wait
for the wind to soften. The time had come.

Innovation & Achievement

1793

Eli Whitney

1

Cotton is little better than a weed. We need a machine. Gentlemen, apply to my young friend, Mr. Whitney. He can make anything.

Of all the post-Revolutionary Americans who grew up without knowing the name for what they felt within themselves, Eli Whitney had the most tortuous career. Yet more than any other one man, he shaped the opposing faces of both the North and South for a half-century to come.

The impact of innovation on history

By 1790 slavery was a declining institution in America. Apart from tobacco, rice, and a special strain of cotton that could be grown only in very few places, the South really had no money crop to export. Sea Island cotton, so named because it grew only in very sandy soil along the coast, was a recent crop and within a short time was being cultivated wherever it found favorable conditions. Tobacco required more care and required reclamation of the soil. However, land was so cheap that planters never bothered to reclaim the soil by crop rotation – they simply found new land farther west. The other crops – rice, indigo, corn, and some wheat – made for no great wealth. Slaves cost something, not only to buy but to maintain; and some Southern planters thought that conditions had reached a point where a slave's labor no longer paid for his maintenance.

Jefferson and Washington were not untypical of their times in their attitude towards slavery; it was a cruel system, and the sooner the South was free of it, the better everyone would be. Some slaves were freed; and many masters, including the more humane, planned on manumission at their own deaths.

Whitney stands at the head of a long line of imaginative Americans who have developed our industry

Whitney came south in 1793, when the Southern planters were in their most desperate plight. In ten days he worked the most fateful revolution in a regional economy that had ever occurred. Floods and earthquakes are cataclysmic; but their effects are forgotten and the scarred earth heals. Whitney's cataclysmic invention was the start of an avalanche. In the South, nothing was ever to be the same again.

Whitney's boyhood was precocious in a way that his neighbors could not comprehend. He had an instinctive understanding of mechanisms. It was a medium in which he could improvise and create in exactly the same way that a poet handles words or a painter uses color.

During his youth, the tall, heavy-shouldered boy with large hands and a gentle manner was a blacksmith, a nail maker on a machine he made at home; and at one time, he was the country's sole maker of ladies' hatpins.

In his early twenties, Whitney determined to attend Yale College, so unusual a step for anyone not preparing for either the law or theology that his parents objected. He was twenty-three before he got away from home and twenty-seven when he received his degree, almost middle-aged in the eyes of his classmates. Again the most serious drawback facing him was that no profession existed suited to a man of his talents. Whitney settled for teaching (he had taught while attending Yale), and accepted a position as a tutor in South Carolina that promised a salary of one hundred guineas a year.

He sailed on a coasting packet that took a few passengers, among whom was the widow of the Revolutionary general, Nathanael Greene. The Greenes had settled in Savannah after the war. When Whitney arrived, he found to his disgust that the promised salary was going to be halved. He not only refused to take the post, but decided to give up teaching as well. Mrs. Greene invited him to accompany her to her plantation and read law. In the meantime, he could make himself useful in one way or another helping the plantation manager, Phineas Miller, whom she intended to marry. Miller was a Yale alumnus, a few years older than Whitney. Whitney accepted the offer.

The need spawned the idea

Shortly after he settled down, some neighbors visited the plantation and, as usual, fell to discussing the bad times. There was no money crop; the only variety of cotton that would grow in that neighborhood was the practically useless green seed variety. Ten hours of handwork was needed to separate one pound of lint from three pounds of the small tough seeds. Until some kind of machine could be devised to do the work, the green seed cotton was little better than a weed.

"Gentlemen," said Mrs. Greene, "apply to my young friend, Mr. Whitney. He can make anything."

At the urging of Mrs. Greene and Phineas Miller, Whitney watched the cotton cleaning and studied the hand movements. One hand held the seed while the other hand teased out the short strands of lint. The machine he designed simply duplicated this.

To take the place of a hand holding the seed, he made a sort of sieve of wires stretched lengthwise. More time was consumed in making the wire than in stringing it because the proper kind of wire was nonexistent.

To do the work of the fingers which pulled out the

lint, Whitney had a drum rotate past the sieve, almost touching it. On the surface of the drum, fine, hook-shaped wires projected which caught at the lint from the seed. The restraining wires of the sieve held the seeds back while the lint was pulled away. A rotating brush which turned four times as fast as the hook-covered drum cleaned the lint off the hooks. Originally Whitney planned to use small circular saws instead of the hooks, but the saws were unobtainable. That was all there was to Whitney's cotton gin; and it never became any more complicated.

A dramatic demonstration

Whitney gave a demonstration of his first model before a few friends. In one hour, he turned out the full day's work of several workers. With no more than the promise that Whitney would patent the machine and make a few more, the men who had witnessed the demonstration immediately ordered whole fields to be planted with green seed cotton. Word got around the district so rapidly that Whitney's workshop was broken open and his machine examined. Within a few weeks, more cotton was planted than Whitney could possibly have ginned in a year of making new machines.

The usual complaint of an inventor was that people were reluctant to give his machine a chance. Whitney's complaint was just the opposite. Before he had a chance to complete his patent model, or to secure protection, the prematurely planted cotton came to growth. With harvests pressing on them, the planters had no time for fine points of law or ethics. Whitney's machine was pirated without a qualm.

Whitney had gone into partnership with Miller. The agreement was that Whitney was to go north to New Haven, secure his patent, and begin manufacturing machines, while Miller was to remain in the South and see that the machines were placed. Having no precedent of royalty arrangement to go on, the partners' first plan was that no machine was to be sold, but simply to be installed for a percentage of the profit earned. Since they had no idea that cotton planting would take place in epidemic proportions, they did not know they were asking for an agreement that would have earned them millions of dollars a year. It had been Miller's idea to take one pound of every three of cotton, and the planters were furious. Cotton, one of the easiest growing crops, was coming up out of the ground in white floods that threatened to drown everyone.

By the time Whitney and Miller were willing to settle for outright sale or even a modest royalty on every machine made by someone else, the amount of money due them was astronomical. He and Miller were now deeply in debt and their only recourse was to go to court; but every court they entered was in cotton country. At length in 1801, eight years after the holocaust started, Miller and Whitney were willing to settle for outright grants from cotton-growing states in return for which the cotton gin would be public property within the boundaries. Even at that, only one state made a counter offer of half the asking price. Whitney accepted the price of $50,000 for which he received a down payment of $20,000 and no more.

The following year, North Carolina followed along in a slightly different fashion, levying a tax on every gin in the state. This sum, less 6 percent for collection, went to Whitney and Miller; it came to another $20,000. Tennessee paid about $10,000, and there was another $10,000 from other states. The gross income was $90,000, most of which was owed for legal costs and other expenses. In 1803, the states repudiated their agreements and sued Whitney for all the money paid to him and his partner.

That year alone the cotton crop earned close to ten million dollars for the planters. The price of slaves had doubled, and men's consciences no longer troubled them. Manumission was a forgotten word.

The following year, 1804, Whitney applied to the federal Congress for relief and, by one vote, was saved from total ruin. He was penniless, his patent was worthless, he was thirty-nine years old, and most of the past ten years had been wasted either in courtrooms or in traveling from one court to another.

He turned his back on cotton, the cotton gin, and the South forever.

Whitney resolved to start over

Returning to New Haven, he resolved to start over. He did not know at first in which direction to go, but he was about to enter the less celebrated but most fruitful time of his life; and just as he had changed the face of the South, he was now about to mold the face of the North into a form it has kept ever since. He was to lay the foundation and invent the techniques for what has become known as the "American System of Manufacture."

* * *

In the early American republic, there was only a handful of skilled machinists. Better than anyone, Whitney knew how small that number was. He then proceeded to invent something far more important than a machine; he invented a system of manufacture which would permit an unskilled man to turn out a product that would be just as good as one made by the most highly trained machinist. He put this system to work on the manufacture of rifles. Without a factory, without even a machine, he persuaded the U.S. government to give him an order for ten thousand muskets at $13.40 each, to be delivered within two years. Only Whitney's prestige as the inventor of the cotton gin could have swayed the government to make such a commitment. From anyone other than Whitney, the claim would have sounded insane.

Until then, every rifle had been made by hand from stock to barrel; but the parts of one gun did not fit any other gun, nor did anyone expect them to. It was Whitney's idea to make all the parts of his rifles so nearly identical that the machined parts could be interchangeable from one gun to another. He did this by designing a rifle. For each part of the gun, a template was made. This was identical in principle to the dress pattern. A man would follow this pattern in cutting a piece of metal. Whitney then had to invent a machine that would allow a man to cut metal according to a pattern. The metal plate to be cut was clamped to a table, the template to be followed would be clamped on top of the metal, and a cutting tool would follow the outlines of the template. Ordinarily, a chisel would be such a tool. A chisel, however, required skill. Whitney took an iron wheel and cut teeth into the circumference so that it looked like a gear. However, the edge of each tooth was curved slightly, sharpened to a cutting edge and then hardened. As the wheel rotated, one tooth after another came into play. Each tooth was then a separate chisel, but each chisel stroke was exactly the same, and the rotation of the wheel gave a steady cutting stroke. This wheel with its cutting teeth was then driven around the edge of the template. No great mechanical skill was needed.

The concept of interchangeable parts

This invention, subordinate to the entire system, was itself a major innovation. It was called the milling machine, and remained unchanged in principle for a century and a half. For the various duties, Whitney designed many different varieties of millers. Before a single workman walked into his factory, Whitney worked out and built all the machinery he would need for his method of production.

Whitney's New Haven friends had put up bonds amounting to thirty thousand dollars. He himself borrowed from the New Haven bank the sum of ten thousand dollars. The money involved in the order, $134,000, made it the biggest single financial transaction in the country. At the end of the first year, he was just getting into production, a marvelous feat by any standards; but instead of the four thousand muskets he had promised, there were only five hundred to show. A commission from Washington handed in an unfavorable report and Whitney's backers looked drawn and thoughtful.

Almost eight years was required for Whitney to fill the order, because practice still showed many gaps in his system. The number of details seemed endless. However, most of the ten thousand were turned out in the last two years. In 1811, Whitney took an order for fifteen thousand, and these were turned out within only two years.

The essence of true creativeness

Whitney was a man on a large scale. There would have been every reason for him to have been embittered by his experience with the cotton gin, but he was too full of the essence of true creativeness. His letters to Robert Fulton describing his experiences are full of remembered anger, but it was the anger of a man who was fighting. His friendships were warm and they lasted. He gambled on his talent, but in the way an artist does.

Like Hamilton, he believed that the factory was to be a benefit to America. Unlike Benjamin Thompson, he did not despise the people who worked in his factories. He also invented a pattern for the relationship between factory owner and the working hands; but of all his inventions this was the shortest-lived. Within a decade after his death, the American factory began to turn into something quite different from Whitney's design.

The same forces that overwhelmed him in the days of the cotton gin were to engulf the American factory.

* * *

Consider Whitney's life and work. His talent for originality, his ambitions, and his solid, merited success are easily encompassed; equally understandable are the directions and limitations imposed by the needs of his society and the tools which previous artisans had put into his hands—consider all this, and add the colors proper to his personal pilgrimage, and still his life and work appear remote. They seem to have been finished long ago; they are even pervaded by the condescending quality of quaintness. These are tricks wrought by time and modern complexities.

His career had been short—only thirty years of intensive effort—but it was to have a long sequel.

The Whitney legacy

Whitney began his work in a nation newly formed, a nation whose founders (save only for the West-Indian-born Hamilton) sought to perpetuate an independent yeoman agriculture and an energetic commercial trade—economies in which they had been reared and in which they had prospered. Just twenty years after the Constitution had been adopted, Whitney completed his first musket contract, and the two streams of force flowing from his work were ready to help reshape American society—two streams destined to come into partial conflict. Eli Whitney of the cotton gin, which gave to the southern plantation system and chattel slavery dominion over hundreds of thousands of square miles, was also Eli Whitney of the standardization of machined parts, which gave to the North, and eventually the whole nation, a dynamic industrialism – a quantity production of inexpensive goods that lifted the standard of well-being, and uniformity of consumption that went far to knit the population into a homogeneous whole. From the one stream of force came national disunity; from the other came progressive integration.

Implicit in many of his letters is his awareness of the sharp difference between Georgia and Connecticut, between white cotton fields and whirring shops, between the agrarian ideas of Governor James Jackson and the Hamiltonian aims of Secretary Oliver Wolcott. When his final illness gave him time for contemplation, did he wonder about the future of these diverse segments of America? Whitney had not intended to affect the ultimate destiny of the South – but he had; he had not intended to remake the national economy and outlook – but to that, too, he had contributed significantly.

The drama at Mulberry Grove

There was drama at Mulberry Grove when Whitney (the Yankee schoolmaster, as he must have been called by the planters who visited there) put a few bolls of upland cotton into his crude, makeshift model, turned the crank, and demonstrated to Miller and the assembled Greene family how the fiber could be torn from its green seeds. That moment proclaimed the future cotton belt, three hundred miles wide and reaching fifteen hundred miles deep to the 97th meridian; sun and rain and heat in proper proportions for cotton's growth set it apart and made it a region distinct, a region which within half a century would arrogate to itself the privileges (it even claimed the divine right) of king of the world's commerce. The gin turned cotton cultivation into a Golconda; in time the crop required more than 25,000 gins.

As with his invention of the cotton gin, so also his contract for muskets with standardized, interchangeable parts ushered in events remarkable and far-reaching. In Whitney's work, manufacturing gins had been the antecedent necessary to project quickly and surely the possibilities of mass-producing muskets. Had he not lost in the factory fire "several machines that were used for different purposes"; simple machines, no doubt, yet specialized and designed for a uniform output? The machines which he mentioned in his arresting proposal to Wolcott, three years later, were even then, in an inner vision, already made. The delay which beset him in fitting up his manufactory with machines was the same kind of perplexing and irritating delay met with in *tooling-up* American munitions plants in 1941-1943. Once the machines were installed, once the tooling-up was completed, the problem was solved; production came with a rush.

Events remarkable and far-reaching

The concept of standardizing parts so that they would be interchangeable did not originate with Whitney alone. Yet, independently, he conceived the idea, as did also Leblanc and Bentham and Brunel. Here the question of priority is misleading – independent invention by three widely separated men is not unique. What can be asserted is that in America Whitney was the first to make the concept into an industrial system.

He laid a primitive but broad foundation; on it, part by part, was built the industrial edifice which has made the United States. After Whitney comes a procession of men who developed his initial masterly achievement. Samuel Colt's first sizable order for revolvers was produced in the Whitney shops (the management having been but recently assumed by Whitney's son), where special machinery was devised to make the intricate parts of the six-shooter.

Isaac M. Singer's mass-produced sewing machines were young industrial America's first calling cards left in homes throughout the world; their accuracy of performance, delicacy of finish, and numerous parts set a level of achievement never before attained. Cyrus H. McCormick and his rivals mass-produced agricultural implements that revolutionized northern farming. The new shoe machinery of Lyman Blake manufactured footgear in quantity and in time to equip the armies of Grant and Sherman. Each utilized the skills of his predecessors, each added important new ideas. The procession is long, varied, impressive; it leads directly to Henry Ford, modern precision methods, and efficiency engineering of which Whitney could not even have dreamed.

An uninterrupted, mighty sequel to Whitney's short career! His genius, his skill, his persistence became the puissant forces by which, in the developing republic, unity defeated disunity, uniformity replaced diversity, technical expertness supplanted a haphazard rule of thumb, and *plenty* was empowered to conquer *want*.

* * *

Estate, will, and codicil of Eli Whitney

Not Whitney's estate, which was impressive, nor the will by which he extended his protecting care to his widow and three children distinguishes Whitney from other rich, responsible men of his period. The codicil, framed with his last living strength, provided his manufactory with trained and devoted supervision; it became the instrument by which the system he had pioneered remained intact and functioning without interruption.

Whitney left considerable wealth. The inventory of his estate made a year after his death, was appraised by Baldwin, his lawyer, Elisha Munson, an astute New Haven merchant, and James Carrington, the government inspector who later became Whitney's foreman; the total for the items listed was $63,085.37. (They had written off the $18,200 Whitney had paid for 174 shares of Eagle Bank stock as a loss. Nine months after his death the bank failed.) Not included in the inventory were other items of value: his personal property, his "Plate and all household articles & implements; my Horse, Chaise & Sleigh, with the articles belonging to the same; . . . also my Watch & all my wearing apparel; . . . my Books, except Rees's Cyclopedia, the Repertory of Arts and Manufactures and such others as relate to the Physical sciences which I give to my son Eli & leave in her care to be delivered to him," which were given without inventory to his wife; nor did the inventory include almost $70,000 Whitney held in personal notes – he, who had known the anguished need to borrow, seemed never to have refused a loan to friend or workman, associate or relative. Also missing was an appraisal of a most valuable but intangible part of the estate – the gun manufactory's goodwill and earning capacity. How could they assess its worth? At best the arms trade was uncertain; Whitney's illness had injured the business; the executors had been forced to ask the government to postpone the first delivery under the new contract for two years, from January, 1824, to January, 1826; and the capacity of his nephews to continue the work still had to be proved.

The importance of his estate, even with those sizable omissions, can best be judged by a measuring stick scaled to times when a skilled New England millwright or carpenter earned $1.25 a day and the roster of rich New Yorkers included the merchant Archibald Gracie (worth $45,000) and the iron dealer Peter P. Goelet (worth $79,000).

Of the appraised amount, the manufacturing plant accounted for almost one-half the inventory: $20,000 was the valuation placed on the two hundred acres containing the Mill Rock site, with three old houses, a new barn, five stone dwellings built for workmen, and worth $1,250 each, "beautifully constructed, and arranged and a stone store;" while the "water privileges, Dam, Bridge, Manufacturing and other buildings and appurtenances thereon exclusive of Machinery" added another $9,500. Real estate and investments–houses and lots in New Haven, "one sixth part of the distillery on Water Street," a small tract of salt meadow, a piece of woodland, a half-interest in a paper mill with its acreage, "millseat privileges and appurtenances"–accounted for $22,000. The balance consisted of farm stock, farm tools and, as the lengthy, detailed inventory shows, materials, tools, and machines used in manufacturing.

From this precise accounting of the contents of the factory at the time of his death, a picture of the arms establishment can be pieced together. It complements Silliman's allusions to a canal Whitney constructed "to take the water from the dam to the forging shop," or the stone work laid in cement composed "of a mixture of iron rust and siliceous and micaceous sand, derived from the grinding of the gun barrels and other pieces of iron," or the two "buildings for fuel: the one for charcoal, and the other for mineral coal. . . These storehouses stand by the side of the mountain and at its foot, and by excavating a road in the bank above, the coal carts are driven up to the gable end . . . and their loads are discharged into them by simply tipping up the cart."

He must have continued to use one of the three old houses as his office; there he kept the master jigs and fixtures, patterns and molds and gages, and supplies of rasps, chisels, augurs, and files of all lengths and shapes–smooth, round, square, bastard, whipsaw. The machine and filing shop shared a building; the list mentions "lathe tools, Milling tools & nitching Machine, Drilling machine: caps & appurtenances, Large cast iron Shears New, Screw Machine & apparatus, Stamping Machine 7 tools, 2 Polishing Machines, Breeching vice & tools, Stake & block for Cutting files"–most of the costly items. In another two-story building, the "stocking shop," were quantities of wood and metals, stores of old copper and copper tubing, fence pickets, pine boards and mahogany, English blistered steel, Milan steel and Russian iron, a huge pile of bullhide leather, a box of asphalt, glue by the pound, squares of glass for replacement, a grindstone with frame and crank–more than a hundred separate articles. A forging shop had seven pairs of bellows, anvils for swedging, "1 Set Bayonet forging tools, 1 Set tools to make tumblers, Heading Stake with five heading tools." A lumber yard stacked with piles of cedar posts and timber blocks was situated between the coal houses and the "White Stone Store." This, with two additional ones–the "Barn Store in New Township" and the "Wooster Store in New Township"–held great quantities of cordage, castings, gun stocks, seasoned boards for musket boxes, supplies of milled screws, a Rumford cooking apparatus, and "33 large 33 less and 33 small boxes supposed to contain 66 cotton-gins"–a motley assortment of articles used or discarded, supplies for a going concern, imperfect parts rejected and junked.

In his will Whitney discharged certain obligations clearly and directly. He stipulated that on the house to be built for his widow the large sum of $6,000 was to be spent. No. 80 Elm Street was to be a mansion.

He and Henrietta had lived in a *hired house* at 275 Orange Street, though for some years he had planned to erect a suitable home and had bought the lot. He provided a handsome yearly allowance for his family, designated which business properties his son was to inherit and what moneys his daughters would receive on marriage, and arranged an annuity for his sister and cash bequests to her daughters. Other obligations, other properties were not so easily arranged.

In January, 1823, serious illness showed Whitney that he could no longer postpone discussing these problems with his lawyer. Minutes made by Baldwin of their conversation reveal Whitney's concern:

"He lamented that so much of (his property) was in real & unproductive estate. He said he had long intended to make some provision for his Nephews, particularly Philos & Eli W. Blake–but he was desirous rather of placing them in a situation to earn for themselves, than to give them much outright–& with that in view he had been repairing the works at his manufactory & intended to complete the repairs & begin work & to add some new machinery & let them in as partners together with Capt. (Jacob) Whiting upon the new contract which they soon expected to commence."

Over the next two years, Whitney's plans crystallized; the day before he died, having resolved the problems, he signed the codicil to the will.

The codicil was a grand proposal to the nephews to carry on the business and complete the third contract–15,000 muskets to be delivered at the rate of 3,000 a year.† Whitney's terms were so advantageous, and made the nephews party to such benefits, that, even had they not remained out of loyalty, self-interest would have dictated their continuing. Eli Blake, who had assisted his uncle during his last illness, and in the unsettled period after his death managed the arms factory and met the first delivery date of 500 guns as stipulated, only confirmed his position when, with Philos, he entered into an agreement with the executors and trustees. This agreement, made on September 23, 1828, gave legal form to the provisions suggested by Whitney. Each nephew was to receive an annual wage of $400 plus a yearly advance of $500 against profits and, on final settlement, two-ninths of the profits made on the contract. They were expected to make all routine repairs. On their part, the trustees were to furnish an adequate working capital, and pay for any extraordinary repairs necessitated by "fire, flood, or any act of God." The Blakes knew how substantial were the moneys they might expect; their combined advances of $1,000 a year would be more than covered by their four-ninths of the profits.

The Blake brothers showed how careful, how thorough had been their uncle's teaching. Not only did they capably execute the contract, they sought to improve the individual parts as before them Whitney had constantly done. It was to justify this—continuing Whitney's unceasing efforts to better the workmanship—not to boast of their abilities, that animated their telling a trustee, "The bolts, screws, and wipers which have been made at this establishment latterly are far superior to those made at any other establishment either public or private."

Whitney's judgment was vindicated by the success

---

†Account books and balance sheets have disappeared. On December 17, 1830, Eli Blake accounted to the trustees for 10,500 muskets: 1,000 delivered in 1827, 3,500 in 1828, 3,000 in 1829, and the final 3,000 in 1830. Since this statement does not include 500 guns delivered on January 1, 1826, the 4,000 muskets remaining on the contract, for which there is no record, might have been delivered between that date and August, 1827, the date Blake's statement begins.

with which the Blakes, brought up to understand mechanical arts and business practices, fulfilled the terms of the contract. Their account, submitted to the trustees, for the period covering August 12, 1827, to November 23, 1830, states that of the $134,031 paid by the government for 10,500 muskets, the costs aggregated $91,200. This schedule of items – it is not bookkeeping in the modern sense of indicating profit and loss, but rather a record of transactions: purchases, rentals from mill houses, wage payments, interest rates, farm expenses, miscellaneous expenditures and receipts – indicates that the margin of profit was $42,831. Under the agreement it was divided, giving four-ninths, or almost $19,000, to the estate, and the same amount to Philos and Eli Blake. Jacob Whiting received one-ninth. Whitney's estate profited as handsomely as did his nephews.

Innovation & Achievement

1807

Robert Fulton

2

In the beginning, she was simply called the *Steamboat*. There was, in the world, no other.

Excerpts from "Robert Fulton," a biography, by Cynthia Owen Philip

The idea of propelling boats by steam dates as far back as the ancient Greeks. Periodically revived, it did not become practicable until advances in metallurgy and mechanics made the invention of a strong, light steam engine possible. During the last quarter of the eighteenth century a flurry of experimentors in England, France, and the United States designed steamboats. Most of them split apart and sank at the first trial. A few, such as John Fitch's, ran briefly but could not be duplicated.

Robert Fulton was the first to build a reliable steamboat. He alone possessed the vision, technical brilliance, entrepreneurial skills and sheer perseverance to make steam navigation a commercial success. Fulton undertook almost every aspect of the work himself, for, in the early 1800s when he was establishing his steamboat empire, there was neither a specialized labor pool nor the management techniques necessary to operate a long term capital-demanding enterprise. Fulton not only designed and supervised the construction of his boats, he also attended to day-to-day operations, financing, marketing, planning for growth and lobbying of government officials. Driven by his dream of a vast transportation system linking the burgeoning country with strong bonds of commerce, he continually risked his reputation, his money and even his life.

His successes helped catapult the U.S. into the forefront of the technological age

Fulton never claimed to have originated the idea of steam navigation, but, as he so eloquently wrote, he did "sit down among the levers, screws, wedges, and wheels like a poet among the letters of the alphabet, and, making a new arrangement transmit a new idea to the world." In doing so he catapulted the United States to the forefront of the technological age.

* * *

The Steamboat's maiden voyage

On August 16, Fulton took the steamboat from the East River boat yard where she was built around the Battery to the dock on the North River near the State Prison in Greenwich Village. The transfer to the new berth was accomplished without the slightest mishap. The steamboat, wrote the wife of Senator Samuel Latham Mitchill, was a curious-looking thing that "rolled through the water by her two great arms, resembling the wheels of a Grist Mill," and would "frighten some of the Old Dutchmen half out of their wits. They will conclude the enemy is coming in earnest with a machine to blow them all up." To Charles Willson Peale's son Rembrandt, she seemed like a huge paddling tortoise. Fulton thought she was quite perfect – the work of an inventive genius. Confident that she would perform well, he was determined to set forth for Albany the next day – Monday, August 17, 1807 – when the almanacs told him high tide was at eight o'clock and would begin its flood again shortly before two in the afternoon. The sun would not set until 6:48, and the moon, rising at 4:38, would be full.

The dock was a good two miles north of City Hall,

but everyone in the metropolis who could possibly do so paraded to the site. Few had any acquaintance with steam engines, and the notion that such a contraption could propel a boat was considered crackpot, irresponsible, or possibly suicidal. The enormous wheels and long, thin proportions were at best comical, for a proper Hudson River craft had an oversized gaff rig and was broad of beam. Dire predictions were interspersed with gleeful jests about "Fulton's Folly." When the chimney began to belch black smoke, bets were on that the entire absurdity would blow up or be claimed by the devil himself.

Dire predictions were interspersed with gleeful jests about "Fulton's Folly"

Fulton missed none of the jibes, but he did not allow them to distract him. In a clear, high voice that carried over the hubbub, he gave precise orders to his engineer, an Englishman named George Jackson for whom he had great respect, and to his captain, Davis Hunt, who was of questionable character, but who at least had the courage to sign on.

It was one o'clock, almost an hour before the turn of the tide, when the "Folly" cast off from the wharf with only the inventor and his skeleton crew aboard. The breeze was against her, but it was light as she began her 150-mile journey. Without faltering, her splashing paddle wheels pushed against the downflowing river. At first, her progress was slow, but as the tide changed, it visibly quickened and she "overtook many sloops and schooners beating to windward and passed them as if they had been at anchor." Within two hours, the steamboat's distant form, dwarfed by the imperial Palisades, could be seen from the wharf only as a banner of black smoke. As night fell and the tide turned against her, she entered wide Haverstraw Bay. The luminous August moon was high as her vibrating, spark-throwing engines thrust her through the narrow waters of the Highlands, past the rugged promontory at West Point. Toward mid-morning on August 18, as the steamboat rounded the bend at Kingston, the hazy blue-green Catskills signaled her approach to Clermont, the country seat of Fulton's aristocratic partner Robert R. Livingston. The tide was with her again, and at precisely one o'clock in the afternoon she faultlessly steamed up to Livingston's private landing and dropped anchor. "Time 24 hours, distance 110 miles," he wrote in his remarkably laconic account for the press. The steamboat had achieved just over 4½ miles an hour, powered only by her engines.

Time 24 hours, distance 110 miles

It has been said that Livingston arranged a splendid gathering "on this day of crowning glory" and prophesied that the name of the inventor would descend to posterity as a benefactor to the world. Celebration there must have been, for as the proprietor of so vast a domain, Livingston would have thought it fitting to share the culmination of his twenty-year dream with his clan and his neighbors and tenants. There is, however, no record of it. All that is known is that, despite the uninterrupted tension and labor of the previous days, Fulton put the engines in motion for the last 40 miles of the journey at 9:13 the following morning, August 19. Livingston, accompanied by his son-in-law Edward and the dean of Ripon Cathedral, boarded for what was to him a delightful outing. Against a pleasant head of wind the steamboat churned through the ebb tide for 8 miles. She then took the flood tide, and just after five o'clock arrived at Albany. "Without any accident or interruption what ever," she achieved almost 5 miles an hour. "She is unquestionably the most pleasant boat I ever went in," the English prelate reported to his compatriots. "In her the mind is free from suspense. Perpetual motion authorizes you to calculate on a certain time to land; her works move with all the facility of a clock; and the noise when on board is not greater than that of a vessel sailing with a good breeze."

Led by the governor, an Albany contingent that had been no more credulous than the New Yorkers stood on the waterfront to greet the vessel propelled by steam. For them the anticipation of disaster was magnified, for that summer a ferry had sunk in the harbor and thirty passengers drowned. Astonishingly, there is no mention of the boat's arrival in the newspapers, but the sheer novelty of the event must have occasioned a fete for the heroes that evening.

Led by the governor, an Albany contingent stood on the waterfront to greet the vessel propelled by steam

Fulton was exhausted. The physical and emotional strain had so drained him that he could scarcely walk. It was, he later said, the turning point of his destiny, the first actual recognition of his usefulness to his fellow man.

At the moment, however, Fulton had no time for reflection or respite. The next morning he hung a placard on the side of the boat announcing the steamboat would start for New York the following day, fare $7.00–over twice as much as the sloops charged. His men laid in provisions–bread, sauce, fowls, liquor, a barrel of water, and a table. Ignoring Fulton's orders, Captain Hunt took gaping sightseers aboard at a shilling a head. But so great was the fear of the boiler exploding, that, in addition to Livingston and the dean, only two Frenchmen dared the return trip–the distinguished botanist François André Michaux and his companion, a French army officer named Parmentier.

Only two Frenchmen dared the return trip

The steamboat left Albany at nine o'clock on Thursday morning and arrived at Clermont at six in the evening. Again there was a light wind against her, but no waves. News traveled fast by word of mouth, and Livingston proudly wrote his son-in-law

Robert: "at Hudson, & indeed at every publick landing the sight was amusing. All the people of the town were upon the hills that bound the river, upwards of twenty boats filled with men & women came to meet us having seen us at a great distance coming down. They all made the utmost efforts to keep up with us & thus there was in the number a five-oared barge double manned. They could not by all their efforts keep near us more than two minutes. She has exceeded Fulton's and justified my calculations."

The whole country talked of nothing but the sea monster, belching forth fire and smoke

After a scant hour's layover, during which Livingston and the dean disembarked, Fulton started for New York. From the riverbanks along the way, excited citizens waved their handkerchiefs and cheered. At West Point the whole garrison turned out and sent up repeated huzzahs. Nonetheless, the ominous aspects of the invention did not escape notice. As one acute – though thrilled – witness wrote: "The whole country talked of nothing but the sea monster, belching forth fire and smoke. The fishermen became terrified, and rowed homewards, and they saw nothing but destruction of their fishing grounds, whilst the wreaths of black vapour, and rushing noise of the paddlewheels, foaming with the stirred up waters, produced great excitement amid the boatmen."

Funds and spirit now only wanting

Fulton guided his steamboat into her berth in New York City at four o'clock on Friday afternoon, August 21. Emotionally spent, he could no more than state for the *American Citizen:* "time 30 hours, space run through 150 miles, equal 5 miles an hour." It was only for Livingston that Fulton revived his characteristic enthusiasm. In a hasty note he wrote: "funds and spirit are now only wanting to do the handsomest and lucrative things which have been performed for some years."

The press ignored the momentous first trip of the steamboat, except for Fulton's laconic notice in the *Citizen* and the brief editorial that accompanied it: "We congratulate Mr. Fulton and the country on his success in the steamboat which cannot fail of being very advantageous. We understand that not the smallest inconvenience is felt in the boat, either from heat or smoke." At that time the newspapers were filled with detailed reports of the conspiracy trial of former vice president Aaron Burr, who had allegedly raised a private army with the intention of forming the lands west of the Mississippi into a separate nation. Ironically, Fulton was left on his own to broadcast his vision of a great nation unified by strong bonds of communication. To his beloved friend Joel Barlow who had not come to New York either to wish him godspeed or to congratulate him on his brilliant achievement, he announced his dream of establishing steam navigation in the West in a letter that was intended for – and received – broad publication. Scornfully commenting on the sarcasm he had endured at the outset of his momentous voyage as the way "in which ignorant men compliment what they call philosophers and projectors," Fulton declared that steam would give cheap and quick access to merchandise on the Mississippi, Missouri, and other great rivers, thus "laying open their treasures to the enterprise of our countrymen."

Readying the boat for scheduled service

The next day, Fulton plunged into the work of rendering his boat safer and more suitable for passengers, "boarding all the sides, decking over the boiler and works, finishing each cabin with twelve berths to make them comfortable, and strengthening many parts of the iron work." It was probably then that he changed from coal to wood to fire his boilers. At that time there was no assured source of coal, and wood was still plentiful and relatively cheap.

Fulton's hope was to run a scheduled service for six weeks or two months, beginning on Wednesday, September 2. Incessant rain delayed the caulkers, but on that day Fulton placed an advertisement in the newspaper announcing that the steamboat would leave New York for Albany on Friday, September 4, at six o'clock in the evening and would arrive thirty-six hours later. He hired one Shoek Johnson as the assistant steward, waiter, and pilot at $18 a month, and a black man named Graft Griffin to be the cook and waiter at $15 a month. In anticipation of a good turnout of thirsty and hungry passengers they laid in more brandy and rum as well as bread and butter, beef, fowls, eggs, watermelon, and sugar.

Fulton enrolled the boat as the North River Steam Boat

On September 3, Fulton enrolled the boat at the port of New York as the *North River Steam Boat.* The name was derived from the Hudson, which as it passes Manhattan was called the North River. Fulton was listed as the sole owner, an arrangement that was agreeable to Livingston because Fulton had advanced far more money than he to pay for her. She was certified to be 142 feet in length and $78\frac{71}{95}$ tons. Although this steamboat is virtually always referred to as the *Clermont,* after Livingston's country seat, she was never called by that name during Fulton's lifetime. In the beginning, she was simply called the *Steamboat.* There was, in the world, no other.

The first trip of the *Steamboat* as a commercial passenger boat was an unqualified success. That is not to say that most of the spectators who found places on the piers and rooftops to witness her departure were converts, but she left as scheduled from the more centrally located Powles Hook Ferry dock at the foot of Cortlandt Street with all berths taken. Twelve passengers booked through to

Albany, one embarked for Tarrytown, one for Newburgh, and, together with Fulton, one other for Clermont. The vessel's progress was considered high theater. At every landing, craft of all kinds pulled alongside for a good view. The Fishkill ferry was commandeered especially for the ladies, to whom Fulton is said to have gallantly raised his hat and exclaimed, "That is the finest sight we have yet seen." When a miller shouted he wanted to see where the grindstones were installed on this floating mill, Fulton took him aboard and gave him a thorough lecture on the mechanical arrangements.

The *Steamboat* arrived in Albany at 11:27 on September 5. Her running time was 28 hours, 45 minutes, an hour and a half faster than the initial northbound trip and 6 hours and 33 minutes ahead of schedule. An affidavit, signed by the passengers, one of whom was Selah Strong, the president of the New York City Council, stated that the "accommodations and conveniences on board exceeded their most sanguine expectations."

Six hours and 33 minutes ahead of schedule

In subsequent trips, Fulton was able to maintain this excellent speed. When the wind was favorable, the crew hoisted the sails to supplement the paddle wheels. The sloops sometimes outpaced her, but she was never becalmed. Riding the *Steamboat* became fashionable. Within a month she carried up to ninety passengers each trip, and it was suggested that the Postmaster General engage her to carry mail from New York City to Albany.

Fulton and Livingston had, without question, struck gold. However, it was not to be easily mined. Accidents, most of them deliberately inflicted by jealous sloop captains, were a constant worry. On her return from Albany in the second week of September, the sloop *Fox* rammed her wheels, then went about and hit her again, driving her on to a

Fulton and Livingston had, without question, struck gold

sand bank which broke her axle wheels. Fortunately, no one was hurt. The ladies "behaved like angels;" they regretted only having missed an agreeable voyage. The *Steamboat* did not resume her schedule until September 23. Ten days later she tangled with a sloop in a stiff wind. This time she lost a paddle wheel and was forced to proceed with only one operating which caused her to pitch dangerously.

Blaming these accidents on Captain Hunt's carelessness – he was later said to have been bribed by the sloop captains – Fulton immediately replaced him with Andrew Brink of Esopus. "You must insist on each one doing his duty or turn him on shore and put another in his place," he instructed Brink. "Everything must be kept in order, everything in its place, and all parts of the Boat scoured and clean. It is not sufficient to tell men to do a thing, but stand over them and make them do it. One pair of Quick and good eyes is worth six pair of hands in a commander." When overtaking sailing vessels, Brink must always run under their stern, unless it was certain he could clear their bow by 50 yards or more.

One pair of quick and good eyes is worth six pair of hands

Brink was no more satisfactory than Hunt, and within a few weeks he had been supplanted by Samuel Wiswall of Hudson who proved more faithful and energetic. Nevertheless, Fulton complained to Livingston: "Our Hands are too numerous, their Wages too high, Our fuel more than half too dear and the quantity may be economized."

These repetitive problems began to weary Fulton, who was eager to get on with his patent application and to lay the groundwork for new government-sponsored submarine experiments. By the end of October he was so restless he took the risk of leaving for Washington. The Barlows whom he had not seen for over six months were now living there.

* * *

Having put himself at such a physical – and psychological – distance from Livingston, Fulton was careful to nurture their partnership through a vigorous correspondence. He wrote at length about current operations and future plans, joking that the postage for his letters, which sometimes ran well over ten pages, would have to come out of next year's profits. Because he regarded the *Steamboat*'s service that autumn as an "experiment under every disadvantage" and, in fact, admitted that the present boat was cranky and needed to be 3 or 4 feet wider for stability, he advocated scrapping everything except the engine and building a far larger and more luxurious vessel. Livingston considered that plan rash and told Fulton they would be better off, from a point of view of expense and of flexibility, with two moderate-sized boats. That did not suit Fulton, and he persuaded Livingston to refurbish the *Steamboat* during the winter, run her all spring and summer, then apply the profits to building a sister ship to be launched in time for the 1809 season. This, he told Livingston, "will give us pleasure and time for arrangements. If we put ourselves in a situation to be pressed for money we shall have more Vexation than I would care to suffer for the [$]3000 which might arise from a new boat in one year to which there would be all the trouble and blunders which arise from hurry in Constructing her."

Fulton was careful to nurture his partnership with Livingston

Livingston advanced a flood of ill-conceived mechanical suggestions. For instance, to save money, he proposed a boiler made from wood and leather, lined with lead and covered with a paste, the principal ingredients of which were oxblood and eggwhites. Fulton genially but forcefully replied that no makeshift solutions would be safe.

The only serious divergence of opinion between Fulton and Livingston that autumn concerned how

The only serious divergence of opinion concerned how to protect the enterprise from competition

they would protect their steamboat enterprise from competition. Still an adept lawyer, Livingston was worried that his state monopoly would be endangered if they applied for a U.S. patent, since by so doing they would acknowledge the supremacy of the federal patent law. The courts had not yet clarified the crucial question of whether the states ceded their right to grant exclusive privileges for useful improvements when the federal law was passed, and it was subject to varying interpretations.

Livingston believed that a state grant differed from a federal patent in that it was a contract to fulfill a service rather than a reward for making public a novel and useful mechanism. He argued that the possession of a state monopoly was, like personal property, under the jurisdiction of the state. Moreover, the state retained the right to restrain the use of patented articles within its borders. "Were a man to patent a new musical instrument would that give him the right to play in your garden and set your children dancing when you wished them to study," he queried. Similarly, the state could prevent a mountebank from vending poisonous medicines, even though it permitted the sale of salubrious medicines.

Fulton did not agree. It had always been his private opinion, he replied, that "The law of the United States Authorizes every inventor to Use his invention throughout the whole of the states, and no particular state can prevent him. Hence if a steamboat which should be acknowledged New and different from ours were to appear on the North River we could not prevent her." Because it was valid everywhere in the country, he insisted they secure their invention with a patent. Seeking corroboration for his view, Fulton borrowed a copy of the patent law from William Thornton (the superintendent of the

Patent Office and soon to be one of Fulton's principal rivals) and discussed the problem briefly with him. Thornton, he reported to Livingston, was adamant that the states had no right to grant exclusive privileges to navigate their rivers. However, in case both his and Thornton's interpretations proved wrong, Fulton promised he would say nothing about it in public "for I would not have the idea circulated."

Fulton favored a general patent; Livingston a state monopoly

The best solution, Fulton thought, was that they take out a patent in the usual form for as long as possible. Then in the spring when their boat was running, he would personally examine the Mississippi. "If I find it practicable and profitable for steamboats we could hold out a bait to congress," he wrote Livingston, "let them give us the exclusive right to the Hudson, Mississippi, Ohio and Missouri Or to the Hudson, Mississippi and its waters for 25 or 30 years And we will make the nation a present of the Invention for all the other waters of America." Fulton's real hope was that, because the heavy expenses of building a boat and the still uncertain profits would deter anyone from trying to pirate their invention immediately, they would have about two years' head start, enough time to firmly establish their hegemony in steam navigation.

Fulton's difficulty was that he still could not find the right words and form of presentation that would establish the originality of his invention. Despite his constant past assertions that the "indispensable principles" he had discovered did indeed constitute an original creation, when confronted with the reality of the patent law, he was baffled about how to express his claim. It would require some study, he confessed to Livingston, to make drawings that would plainly show why he had succeeded where all others had failed, "for although the effect produced is new, the whole is composed of old parts and looks as though different persons who have attempted Steam boats had tried the whole of them. You will therefore be so good As to aid me with your Ideas of the distinction which makes the novelty of this invention and renders it superior to all attempts of the kind which have been made."

Fulton's difficulty was in establishing the novelty of his invention

Livingston was unable or unwilling to advise him. His principal contribution to the enterprise was, after all, the possession of the New York State monopoly. In the end he succeeded in convincing Fulton, at least temporarily, that neither their New York monopoly nor their prospective patent was in jeopardy. Not daring to face the patent problem alone, Fulton postponed his plan to file an application until the following spring when he and Livingston would have had a chance to work on it together. Although he did not acknowledge it openly, he was unquestionably dependent on Livingston.

* * *

[Obtaining a patent became critical, for the New York State monopoly was immediately challenged by rivals. Abetted by William Thornton, the superintendent of the Patent Office, they copied Fulton's designs and hired away his workers.

Fulton's personal life was more satisfying. On January 4, 1808, he married Livingston's young cousin Harriet and that summer they moved to Washington to live with the Barlows. In October Harriet presented him with a son, Robert Barlow Fulton.]

Fulton was tempted to go to New York. He was kept in Washington, however, not only by Harriet and the baby, but by his patent application. The novelty criterion was giving him trouble. To meet it—or perhaps to overwhelm it—he compiled an imposing document of over five thousand words together with diagrams, tables, calculations, and twelve plates. The overblown verbal description cost fifteen dollars just to have copied. Although his fundamental concepts dated from the "letters of the alphabet" argument, published in 1796 in his *Treatise on Canals,* he had evolved no convincing way of articulating his conviction that invention consisted of a new combination of existing elements. The message he desperately hoped to convey was that, unlike other inventors of the time, he was not a tinkerer but a sophisticated, systematic experimenter using a comprehensive approach to bring theory into practice. This was indeed true, but the law was designed with discrete machines or processes in mind. Theories were not patentable, no matter how useful they might be.

Fulton was not a tinkerer, but a sophisticated, systematic experimenter

Fulton's description of his invention began with the assertion that the successful construction of a steamboat did not depend on any new form of steam engine or boiler, but on his unique discovery of the principles governing the total steamboat design. By using his formula any intelligent artisan could determine the relationship of engine power, wheel size, and hull dimensions that would use steam most advantageously. Basically, a steamboat's bow would be pointed to at least 60 degrees, the length "such that her friction will equal the plus and minus pressure," and her bottom flat. Paddle wheels were preferable to endless chains or smoke jack flyers – that is, propellers.

To explain how he arrived at his method of finding minimum resistances and velocities, Fulton included the definitions and table evolved by Beaufoy from his experiments at Deptford Dock in the 1790s and published in 1802 in Charnock's *History of Naval Architecture.* In addition, he ran through an exhaustive series of calculations based on the dimensions and machinery of his steamboat, which he illustrated with fourteen figures, tables, and drawings. The first is a rendering of the *Steamboat* passing through a dramatic section of the Highlands, included, perhaps, to satisfy his aesthetic sensibilities but also to remind Thornton his invention was a reality. Another drawing was of a boat breasting powerful rapids by means of a winch worked by her engine, a device he expected would be useful on the Mississippi.

In the course of his text, Fulton frankly admitted that a boat could be propelled by steam even though his exact proportions were not observed and that a stern wheel might be used instead of side wheels, but he insisted that his proportions were necessary to achieve the greatest speed with a given power. "Having been the first to discover and describe the exact principles and proportions on which steamboats should be built, and having given a mechanical combination, the utility of which is proved by practice," he concluded, "I shall consider every attempt to construct such vessels on those principles as an infringement on my rights."

The exact principles and proportions for building steamboats

* * *

[By the spring of 1814 litigation over the monopoly had been brought to a feverish pitch by Aaron Ogden, a former governor of New Jersey who wished to operate a ferry from Manhattan to the Jersey coast, routes contracted for by Livingston's brother. Livingston had died in 1813 and the whole burden of defending their steamboat empire fell on Fulton's shoulders.]

Fulton addressed the State Assembly in his own behalf. Characteristically, he played the role of persecuted genius. Pleading that his invention was obviously new because in the face of disbelief and ridicule he had established the first steamboat line in the world, he pointed out that, because of his labors, the state now possessed the most rapid, cheap, commodious, and elegant conveyance on earth. In contrast, Ogden's sole motivation was to cut in on the profits. Any loss Ogden sustained, therefore, was caused by his own error in judgment and not by the Livingston-Fulton monopoly.

The whole burden of defending the steamboat empire fell on Fulton's shoulders

Informing the Assembly that his company was $77,000 in debt and that it would take five years with four boats in daily service between Albany and New York to break even, Fulton sought the legislators' high-minded sympathy by describing how chilling the violation of inventors' just claims was to the spirit of enterprise.

Fulton then produced depositions from his foreman Charles Staudinger and his agent Benjamin Henry Latrobe and, to reinforce his claim to original invention, he exhibited what he asserted was a true copy of a letter to Lord Stanhope, dated November 4, 1793, in which he discussed using side wheels as a means of propulsion. This evidence, it was reported, gained Fulton many supporters.

The final oration of his lawyer, Thomas Addis Emmet, displayed all the Hibernian theatricality for which he was so famous. Addressing Fulton directly, he warned that, no matter how the present case was decided, "interest and avarice" would always rise against him:

"You rely too implicitly on the strength of your rights, and the sanctity of the obligations on which they are founded. You expect too much from your well-earned reputation, and the acknowledged utility to mankind of your life and labours. You permit your mind to be engrossed with vast and noble plans for the public good. You are inconsiderately sinking your present income in the extension of public accommodation by steamboats. You are gratuitously giving your time and talents to the construction of that great national object, your stupendous invention for maritime defence.

"Artful speculators will assuredly arise, with patriotism on their tongues, and selfishness in their hearts, who calumniating or concealing your merits, will talk loudly of your monopoly–who will present it as a grievous burden on the community, who will exaggerate your fortune. Yes, my friend! my heart bleeds while I utter it; but I have fearful forebodings, that you may hereafter find in public faith a broken staff for your support, and receive for public gratitude, a broken heart for your reward."

The New York State monopoly upheld

On March 30, Ogden was denied his petition by a vote of 51 to 43. The monopoly rights bestowed on Fulton and Livingston were upheld intact. In triumph Fulton wrote to his agent, John Delacy, "I came here to defeat Aaron Ogden's projects which I have done in the most satisfactory manner." But to his friend Cadwallader C. Colden, who had returned to New York before the vote was taken, he wrote, "You happy, happy man to be at home with your wife and family while I am very, very alone."

* * *

[The legal battle was still raging when Robert Fulton died suddenly of pneumonia on February 23, 1815. He was given a hero's burial.]

Reverently Fulton was pronounced a national benefactor. The steamboat network he had established on the Hudson and Mississippi Rivers was unique in the world, and his recently launched steam frigate *Fulton I* promised to make the United States equal to any nation in naval power. "His is the only loss for which the public has no indemnity," the

New-York Evening Post's obituary proclaimed. "Politicians, historians, poets etc. are found throughout the United States, and readily succeed to each other, but there is no person who will succeed to Mr. Fulton's genius as a mechanic, or be capable of prosecuting those schemes which he left in an unfinished state."

There is no person who will succeed to Mr. Fulton's genius

In his eulogy before the American Academy of Arts, DeWitt Clinton declared: "While he was mediating plans of mighty import for his future fame and his country's good, he was cut down in the prime of his life and in the midst of his usefulness. Like the self-burning tree of Gambia, he was destroyed by the fire of his own genius and the never ending activity of a vigorous mind."

* * *

In the years since Robert Fulton's death, the controversy over whether he was a visionary laboring for the benefit of humanity or merely an adventurer serving his own ambitions has not abated. He was, of course, both. A courageous idealist, he was also an opportunist. Fulton did not invent the steamboat—nor did Fitch, Rumsey, or Thornton. But he did "sit down among levers, screws, wedges, and wheels like a poet among the letters of the alphabet and, making a new arrangement, transmit a new idea to the world." Obsessed by his vision of a society harmoniously united by free trade and reliable transportation, he attempted more than he could accomplish. He overreached himself. His ability to do so, however, was the essense of his genius and the foundation of his lasting fame.

Innovation & Achievement

1831

C. H. McCormick

3

At first, nobody even believed, but then I gave the first public demonstration of my reaper, and cut six acres of oats at Steele's Tavern in one day.

By far the most important single step towards the American mechanization of agriculture was Cyrus McCormick's reaper. In the late 1830s, grain had to be imported from Europe to make up for the shortages in the American crop. The shipment of wheat from Chicago amounted to only seventy-eight bushels in 1838. Ten years later, Chicago alone was shipping two million, with every promise that the yield would continue to increase. The economic future of the North was becoming clear, and the defeat of the Confederacy was foreseen by far-sighted Southerners eight years before secession. Except for the political tradition that allowed the South a disproportionately powerful voice in the selection of presidential candidates, the South was on its way to becoming the least important of the nation's three great regions.

A man had to cut with a scythe; an acre a day was a good yield

Wheat was one of the factors that killed the old South. In western soil, wheat was easy to sow and to grow. Reaping was another matter. A man had to cut with a scythe and slowly move down the field, swinging as he went. An acre a day for a strong man was a good average yield. Farmers helped each other to harvest crops, but everyone's wheat came to full growth at about the same time, and there were only about ten days, given good weather, in which the crop could be gathered in. At reaping time, hired hands came high. Until McCormick invented his mechanical reaper, a man grew only as much wheat as he himself could reap by hand. If more grain stood in his field, it was left for the cattle.

The reaper came along exactly when it was needed

McCormick's reaper has no great rank as a feat of creative imagination, but it was introduced at the precise time when it helped to change history in the West where it was needed, where great expanses of land could be put to use if men had the means of gathering all the wheat they could grow. Without the West, McCormick's reaper would have met the same fate as the earlier model of Bell in England. Even in the eastern United States, reapers were only slowly adopted. The uneven rocky land of New England required a far more refined machine than McCormick's early models which were ideally suited to flat prairie. The reaper made the West pay.

In a sense, the Civil War was created by two American machines – the North rolling its frontier westward thirty miles a year behind the McCormick reaper; the South rich and solid on the cotton gin. For a touch of irony, McCormick was born in Virginia; Whitney came from New England.

* * *

Cyrus McCormick was born in 1809 three days after the birth of Lincoln. The McCormick family were prosperous farmers. The father, Robert, was himself an inventor with his own smithy. His son, Cyrus, grew up familiar with the tools of his time, at home in the blacksmith shop on his father's farm.

Robert McCormick's great failure was a mechanical reaper which he finally gave up as hopeless.

Cyrus McCormick, who had always identified himself with his father, was impelled to prove that in this respect, at least, he was more a man than his father. He took over the reaper as his responsibility.

He was a young man with narrow interests and few friends. He held himself aloof from almost everyone, but not because he courted anonymity; a man who dresses with almost dandyish elegance is a man who wants to be noticed.

His younger brothers and sisters used to tease him for being so straitlaced, but secretly they were in awe of him. When he became a millionaire before he was forty, they made no secret of their awe, and he, in return, was very generous.

The young inventor toiled laboriously to complete his reaper in time for the harvest in 1831. He was very nearly too late, but a small patch of wheat was left standing at his request; and one day in July, with no spectators except his parents and his excited brothers and sisters, Cyrus put a horse between the shafts of his reaper, and drove against the yellow grain. The reel revolved and swept the gentle wheat downwards upon the knife. Click! Click! Click! The white steel blade shot back and forth. The grain was cut. It fell upon the platform in a shimmering golden swath. From here it was raked off by a young laborer named John Cash. It was a roughly done specimen of reaping, no doubt. The reel and the divider worked poorly. But for a preliminary test it was a magnificent success. Here, at last, was a reaper that reaped, the first that had ever been made in any country.

Click! Click! Click! The white steel blade shot back and forth

Several days after the advent of the reaper on the home farm, Cyrus McCormick had improved its reel and divider, and was ready for a public exhibition at the nearby village of Steele's Tavern. Here, with two horses, he cut six acres of oats in an afternoon, a feat which was attested in court in 1848 by his brothers William and Leander, and also by three of the villagers, John Steele, Eliza Steele, and Dr. N. M. Hitt. Such a thing at that time was incredible.

Neighbors who had seen earlier performances of the father's reaper admitted that it was "a right curious sort of thing" but "nobody ever believed it would come to much."

The fact that went unappreciated was that horse-power was being substituted for human labor. From that point of view, a reaper is a device which converts the pulling power of a horse into the intelligence, judgment, experience, and strength necessary to harvest a field of standing grain.

It did the work of six men with scythes

It was equal to the work of six laborers with scythes, or twenty-four peasants with sickles. It was as marvellous as though a man should walk down the street carrying a dray-horse on his back.

The next year, 1832, Cyrus McCormick came out with his reaper into what seemed to him "the wide, wide world." He gave a public exhibition near the little town of Lexington, which lay eighteen miles south of the farm. Fully one hundred people were present—several political leaders of local fame, farmers, professors, and laborers, who frolicked and shouted in uncomprehending joy.

At the start, it appeared as though this new contraption of a machine, which was unlike anything else that human eyes had ever seen, was to prove a grotesque failure. The field was hilly, and the reaper jolted and slewed so violently that John Ruff, the owner of the field, made a loud protest.

"Here! This won't do," he shouted. "Stop your horses. You are rattling the heads off my wheat."

This was a hard blow to the young farmer-inventor. Several laborers, who were openly hostile to the machine as their rival in the labor market, began to jeer with great satisfaction. "It is a humbug," said one. "Give me the old cradle yet, boys," said another. These men were hardened and bent and calloused with the drudgery of harvesting. They worked twelve and fourteen hours a day for less than a nickel an hour. But they were as resentful toward a reaper as the drivers of stagecoaches were to railroads, or as the hackmen were towards automobiles.

At this moment of apparent defeat, a man of striking appearance, who had been watching the floundering of the reaper with great interest, came to the rescue.

"I'll give you a fair chance, young man," he said. "That field of wheat on the other side of the fence belongs to me. Pull down the fence and cross over."

This friend in need was the Honorable William Taylor, who was several years later a candidate for the governorship of Virginia. His offer was at once accepted by Cyrus McCormick, and as the second field was fairly level, he laid low six acres of wheat before sundown. This was no more than he had done in 1831, but on this occasion he had conquered a larger and more incredulous audience.

The machine was put on view in the courthouse square

After the sixth acre was cut, the reaper was driven with great acclaim into the town of Lexington and placed on view in the courthouse square. Here it was carefully studied by a Professor Bradshaw of the Lexington Female Academy, who finally announced in a loud and emphatic voice, "This–machine–is worth–a hundred–thousand–dollars." This praise, from "a scholar and a gentleman," as McCormick afterwards called him, was very encouraging. And still more so was the quiet word of praise from Robert McCormick, who said, "It makes me feel proud to have a son do what I could not do."

* * *

Not far from the McCormick homestead was the Old Field School, built of logs and with a part of one of the upper logs cut out to provide a window. Here the boy Cyrus sat on a slab bench and studied five books as though they were the only books in the world,–Murray's Grammar, Dilworth's Arithmetic, Webster's Spelling Book, the Shorter Catechism, and the Bible.

The early years before the invention

He was a strong-limbed, self-contained, serious-natured boy, always profoundly intent upon what he was doing. Even at the age of fifteen he was inventive. One winter morning he brought to school a most elaborate map of the world, showing the two hemispheres side by side. First he had drawn it in ink upon paper, then pasted the paper upon linen, and hung it upon two varnished rollers. This map, which is still preserved, reveals a remarkable degree of skill and patience; and the fact that a mere lad could conceive of and create such a map was a week's wonder in the little community. "That boy," declared the teacher, "is beyond me."

At about this time he undertook to do a man's work in the reaping of the wheat, and here he discovered that to swing a cradle against a field of grain under a hot summer sun was of all farming drudgeries the severest. Both his back and his brain rebelled against it. One thing at least he could do – he could make a smaller cradle, that would be easier to swing; and he did this, whittling away in the evening in the little log workshop.

Cyrus was a natural mechanical genius

"Cyrus was a natural mechanical genius," said an old laborer who had worked on the McCormick farm. "He was always trying to invent something." "He was a young man of great and superior talents," said a neighbor. At eighteen he studied the profession of surveying, and made a quadrant for his own use. This is still preserved, and bears witness to his good workmanship. From this time until his twenty-second year, there is nothing of exceptional interest recorded of him. He had grown to be a tall, muscular, dignified young man. The neighbors, in later years, remembered him mainly because he was so well dressed on Sundays, in broadcloth coat and beaver hat, and because of his fine treble voice as he led the singing in the country church.

No time for gayeties

Even as a youth he was absorbed in his inventions and business projects. He had no time for gayeties. In a letter written from Kentucky to a cousin, Adam McChesney, in 1831, he says: "Mr. Hart has two fine daughters, right pretty, very smart, and as rich probably as you would wish; but alas! I have other business to attend to."

The father's machine became the joke of the neighborhood

Ever since Cyrus was a child of seven, it had been the most ardent ambition of his father to invent a reaper. He had made one and tried it in the harvest of 1816, but it was a failure. It was a fantastic machine, pushed from behind by two horses. A row of short curved sickles was fastened to upright posts, and the grain was whirled against them by revolving rods. It was highly ingenious, but the sinewy grain merely bunched and tangled around its futile sickles; and the poor old reaper that would not reap was hauled off the field, to become one of the jokes of the neighborhood.

This failure did not dishearten Robert McCormick. He persevered with Scotch-Irish tenacity, but in secret. Hurt by the jests of the neighbors, he worked thenceforward with the door of his workshop locked, or at night. He hid his reaper, too, upon a shelf inside the workshop. He allowed no one to see what he was doing, except his sons; and he worked for years to make a reaper. He always kept his plans to himself, and he told his wife that if visitors came to the house, she should send one of the children to fetch him, and not allow the visitors to come to his workshop.

By the early summer of 1831, Robert McCormick had so improved his reaper that he gave it a trial in a field of grain. Again it was a failure. It did cut the grain fairly well, but flung it in a tangled heap. As much as this had been done before by other machines, and it was not enough. To cut the grain was only one-half of the problem; the other half of the problem, which up to this time no one had solved, was how to properly handle and deliver the grain after it was cut.

By this time Cyrus had become as much of a reaper enthusiast as his father. Also, he had been studying out the reasons for his father's failure and working out in his mind a new plan of construction.

Cyrus envisioned a better way

Cyrus took up the work that his father had reluctantly abandoned. He had never seen or heard of any reaper experiments except those of his father; but he believed he saw a better way, and "devoted himself most laboriously to the discovery of a *new principle of operation*."

He showed his originality at the outset by beginning where his father and all other reaper inventors had left off–with the cutting of grain that lay in a fallen and tangled mass. He faced the problem worst end first. The reaper that would cut such grain, he believed, must first separate the grain that is to be cut from the grain that is left standing. It must have at the end of its knife a curved arm–a *divider.* This idea was simple, but in the long history of harvesting grain no one had thought of it before.

Next, in order to cut this snarled and prostrate grain without missing any of it, the knife must have two motions: its forward motion, as drawn by the horses, and also a slashing sideways motion of its own. How was this to be done? McCormick's first thought was to cut the grain with a whirling wheel-knife, but this plan presented too many new difficulties. Suddenly the idea came to him – why not have a straight blade, with a back and forward motion of its own? This was the birth-idea of the *reciprocating blade,* which has been used to this day on all grain-cutting machines. It was not, like the divider, a wholly new conception; but Cyrus McCormick conceived it independently, and did more than any one else to establish it as the basic feature of the reaper.

The birth of the reciprocating blade

The third problem was the supporting of the grain while it was being cut, so that the knife would not merely flatten it to the ground. McCormick solved this by placing a row of *fingers* at the edge of the blade. These fingers projected a few inches, in such a way that the grain was caught and held in position to be cut. The shape of these fingers was afterwards much improved, to prevent wet grain from clogging the slit in which the knife slid back and forth.

A fourth device was still needed to lift up and straighten the grain that had fallen. This was done by a simple revolving *reel,* such as fishermen use for the drying of their nets. Several of the abortive reapers that had been tried elsewhere had possessed some sort of a reel; but McCormick made his much larger than any other, so that no grain was too low to escape it.

The fifth factor in this assembling of a reaper was the *platform,* to catch the cut grain as it fell; and from which the grain was to be raked off by a man who walked alongside of it. The sixth was the idea of putting the shafts on the outside, or stubble side, of the reaper, making it a *side-draught,* instead of a "push" machine. And the seventh and final factor was the building of the whole reaper upon one big *driving-wheel,* which carried the weight and operated the reel and cutting-blade. The grain-side end of the blade was at first supported by a wooden runner, and later – the following year – by a small wheel.

It reaped

Such was the making of the first practical reaper in the history of the world. It was as clumsy as a Red River ox cart; but *it reaped.* It was made on right lines. The new principle that the youth McCormick laboriously conceived in the little log workshop became the basic type of a wholly new machine. It has never been displaced. Since then there have been 12,000 patents issued for reaper and mower inventions; but not one of them has overthrown the type of the first McCormick reaper. Not one of the seven factors that he assembled has been thrown aside; and the most elaborate self-binder of today is a direct descendant of the crude machine that was thus created by a young Virginian farmer in 1831.

* * *

The financial crash of 1837

Shortly after the reaper trial, Robert McCormick gave Cyrus a farm of two hundred acres and took him in as partner in a small iron foundry. In the mid-1830s the price of iron was soaring sky-high. Cyrus McCormick had neither the need nor the incentive to bother with the reaper he had developed. The financial crash of 1837 reached its full effect in Virginia two years later, and the McCormicks were thrown into poverty, losing farm and foundry. For the next five years the father and all the sons worked on the father's farm to pay off pressing creditors.

The financial pressure made McCormick turn once again to his reaper; however, he was driven to perfect it just at the time when other farmers lacked the cash to buy a machine costing over a hundred dollars. The farmers' bankruptcy had similarly smashed the hardware firm of Goodyear and Sons. Both Goodyear and McCormick were driven to invention at the same time and by the same crisis.

In 1841 McCormick finally sold two machines. In the next year he sold seven more. In the next two years he sold eighty. Then McCormick, at the age of thirty-six, with sixty dollars in his pocket, rode out to see the West of Illinois, Ohio, and Indiana. He saw the rolling fields and at once understood where his machine was really needed. For several years, he had machines built and assembled in other men's shops, but in 1847 he selected the small town of Chicago as the site of his own manufactory and talked William Ogden, the mayor, into becoming his partner. He also talked Ogden into putting up fifty thousand dollars. In the next two years the business was so prosperous that McCormick was able to buy him out.

Exploring new markets

McCormick built and sold a thousand reapers in 1851. He won a first prize in the London exposition and became a world figure, a member of the Legion of Honor, and a knight of several minor orders. In 1857, twenty-three thousand machines made him a profit in that one year alone of a million and a quarter dollars.

McCormick had many rivals and competitors. When he wasn't suing them for infringement, they were suing him. In that highly eloquent day, lawsuits were carried on with a ferocity that was merciless. Opposing sides pelted each other to stupefaction with claims and counter-claims, attachments and counter-attachments, writs and restraints.

Rivals and competitors

McCormick fought his rivals to a standstill, and they came back for more. His most serious rival for a time was Obed Hussey, and then later John H. Manny. When the legal battle with Manny came up in 1854, all of McCormick's competitors got together to finance Manny's legal costs; for if McCormick could ruin Manny, he would ruin them all. The Manny backers retained George Harding against McCormick's Edward N. Dickinson, one of the ablest patent lawyers of his day.

The case was to be tried in Springfield, Illinois before Judge Drummond. The Manny backers thought it would be a shrewd move to associate with Harding, a popular local lawyer. They found a man in Springfield who was a close friend of Drummond's, named Abraham Lincoln. Enormous war funds were available for both sides. McCormick was demanding four hundred thousand dollars from Manny as damages.

A young lawyer named Abraham Lincoln

Before the case came to trial, both parties consented to a transfer to Cincinnati. Since this was Lincoln's first big case, he came prepared with a long technical brief; but since the trial was not in Springfield, Lincoln was no longer needed. Without consulting Lincoln, the Manny backers had obtained Edward M. Stanton. The polished elegant eastern lawyers unceremoniously pushed Lincoln aside into the role of spectator. It was Lincoln's deepest humiliation and disappointment. He stayed, however, to earn his fee; and his hurt was overbalanced by his admiration for Stanton's peerless performance during the trial. Although Lincoln stood silent in the courtroom, his one-thousand-dollar fee enabled him to devote more time to politics and to go to the stump soon after for the famous series of debates with Stephen Douglas.

Lincoln never forgot Stanton's brilliance at the trial, and although he and Stanton had never met again, Lincoln swallowed his humiliation and insisted on having Stanton serve in his cabinet.

Until 1858 McCormick lived as always, aloof from people, immersed in the detail of his work and the endless litigation which he apparently enjoyed with gusto. He lived in hotels and on the trains that took him from city to city for endless conferences. The tall, slim, serious-minded dandy of twenty-two had grown into a "massive Thor of Industry." In the mid-1850s his mother died, and in 1858 the most eligible bachelor of Golden Chicago, now forty-nine, portly, and with several millions, finally "succumbed to Cupid's glances" and Miss Nettie Fowler of New York – many years his junior.

The *Chicago Daily Press* said:

"If our townsman . . . has delayed the ceremonies for a few more years than is customary . . . we risk nothing in pronouncing the prize well worth his waiting, and in *reaping* one of the fairest flowers our city can boast, he has but added the orange blossoms to the laurels of his world-famous title of nobility."

McCormick traveled like a mid-nineteenth-century millionaire – like American royalty. He was an indefatigable fighter on any issue, on any scale. In 1862, when his children were very small, he had been in Washington on business with his family. His wife, children, nurses, and servants, and voluminous portmanteaus, valises, and trunks were sent ahead to board the train. At the last moment, McCormick arrived at the station. When he checked his tickets he discovered there was an overcharge of $8.70 on his wife's baggage. To McCormick this was an outrage. He refused to pay. The conductor refused to revise the freight rates. McCormick refused to ride on the train. He called off his family and retinue just as the train began to move. The conductor refused to hold back the train long enough to get off McCormick's luggage. This was *lèse-majesté.* McCormick wired his indignation to the president of the New York Central. The president of the New York Central wired Philadelphia to put off McCormick's luggage when the Washington train came in. The wire was late, the luggage went on to Chicago, was stored in a warehouse; the warehouse was hit by lightning and burned down. It couldn't have happened to a wilder man.

The $8.70 lawsuit

McCormick sued the New York Central for twenty thousand dollars, but withheld the suit until after the war was over; he knew he was unpopular on account of his Southern sympathies. Immediately after the war he hired Roscoe Conkling and won twelve thousand dollars. The New York Central appealed. The case of the $8.70 baggage charge marched from court to court up to the exalted heights of the Supreme Court, which ordered a new trial. More lawyers were retained. On the second trial, McCormick was awarded fifteen thousand dollars. The New York Central appealed all the way back up to the Supreme Court again. Constitutional issues were temporarily set aside as the Court again looked at the volumes of papers referring to McCormick and the brutal train conductor.

Five times the case was tried, each time being battled up to the Supreme Court of the United States. Major political parties and presidential aspirants became involved. After more than twenty years the New York Central gave up, deciding that its main business was not in the law courts.

McCormick had died in 1884, but his estate was awarded his twenty thousand dollars. Even though the costs far exceeded that figure, McCormick's adored and adoring wife, Nettie, knew that her husband had won the victory that was dearest to his heart. She wrote to her son:

"You see, your dear father's course from first to last is . . . vindicated!"

* * *

That young Virginian farmer who awoke from his dream and made his dream come true, made it possible for a few in each country to provide enough food for all. He found a cure for hunger, which had always persisted like a chronic disease. He heaped the plates on the tables of thirty-six nations. He took a drudgery and transformed it into a profession. He instructed the wheat-eating races how to increase the "seven small loaves" so that the multitudes should be fed. He picked up the task of feeding the hungry masses–the Christly task that had lain unfulfilled for eighteen centuries, and led the way in organizing it into a system of international reciprocity.

The dream fulfilled

Innovation & Achievement

1835

Saml. F. B. Morse

4

I was about to give up, but then Gale showed me how to wind the bar of iron. I opened and closed the circuit. The apparatus showed some response.

Men have always found the means to communicate with others at a distance. Bonfires flickered on hill after hill in the darkness of prehistory to signal distant tribes that an enemy was on the way, or that herds of game had moved into new areas. In the seventeenth century, the word *telegraph* came into use when Englishmen began experimenting with semaphore devices. An observer would decipher the signal on a distant hill and then send it on to the next watcher.

A need that originated in the darkness of history

In the late eighteenth century, the Chappé system was perfected. The telegrapher on top of a tower with a spyglass decoded the message signaled from another tower fifteen miles away. He would then go below, crank the semaphore arms of his own instrument, and laboriously relay the message to another tower some fifteen miles farther on. In the United States, lower Cape Cod is still studded with a number of telegraph hills: remnants of the first commercial semaphore system installed and worked by Jonathan Grout in 1800, to transmit from Martha's Vineyard to Boston merchants the news of incoming vessels, their cargo, and their condition.

The young republic wanted a network along the entire Atlantic coast and a prize of thirty thousand dollars was offered for a telegraph system that would be workable for a thousand miles.

A prize of thirty thousand dollars

An accident of history determined that the offer did not qualify the word *telegraph* with the word *semaphore.* After several years of silence from the general public, the government in the late 1830s was surprised to find that its half-forgotten offer had been taken up by a man who proposed to use the word *telegraph* in a very novel way.

The man's name was Samuel Finley Breese Morse.

Both Morse and America had come a long way since the turn of the century. Morse had been born in 1791 in Charlestown, Massachusetts, the son of Jedediah Morse, a famous New England minister. He was a boy at Andover in the same decade in which John Fitch died in despair, when Oliver Evans was being ridiculed by skeptics who refused to believe what he made plain before their eyes. Morse entered Yale in 1807, a few months after Fulton made his voyage to Albany in the *Clermont;* in effect, Morse was growing up with the American myth.

In 1811, he went to England to study art with Washington Allston. As a painter, he showed great promise, but he was trapped by his unquestioning acceptance of the intellectual fashion, then current, that the art which represented scenes of history and antiquity was higher than the art which portrayed living people. On his return to America in 1815, he found himself in a country too raw, too busy, and too poor to recognize or care about an art so far removed from reality. On the other hand, America of 1815 was deeply interested in portraits. By 1817, he was being paid sixty dollars for a picture, and he could complete four a week. He made a tour of the South and in 1818 returned with three thousand dollars, enabling him to marry Lucretia Walker of Concord.

With this capital, he moved to Charleston, South Carolina, gave up portrait work and devoted himself for the next eighteen months to the painting of an enormous historical picture for the House of Representatives at Washington. He failed to sell it. His money was gone, and he moved to New York for a new try. There he was commissioned by the city to go back to Washington to do a full-length portrait of Lafayette who was visiting the country. He did two portraits. All of Morse's portraits show power; but his *Lafayette* was the work of a mature and controlled talent. Still Morse was dissatisfied, even though in the next few years he was to be the acknowledged leader of young American artists. In 1829 he returned to Europe to continue his studies.

Morse the artist: an idea took fire within him

In America, artists who insisted on their *genres* either starved quietly, or else, like the Peales, opened private museums to display their wares along with other curiosities of the day. Taking his cue from the Peales, Morse decided to paint the sort of picture which would interest an America that had never seen either the original or copies of the *Mona Lisa, The Last Supper,* or any of the other masterpieces of the world of art. He painted *The Louvre* which showed for background as many of the masterpieces hanging in that museum as he could cram in. Full of hope, in 1832, he packed his canvases and returned to America on the packet *Sully.* He boarded the ship a painter, and disembarked an inventor.

Aboard the *Sully,* Morse got into a conversation about European experiments on electromagnetism. The work of Faraday had been published only a few months earlier and had at once been duplicated in most European laboratories. "Drawing sparks from a magnet" was one of the scientific marvels of the

He held the belief that Americans could do anything they set their minds to

moment. Morse immediately suggested that a combination of sparks could be used as a code to send messages over a wire. The idea took fire within him, although he was almost totally ignorant of the most basic principles of electricity. Morse, by this time, was also ridden by the witch of belief that Americans could do anything they set their minds to. Lack of background meant nothing–God would provide. He had spent twenty years studying the art of painting; yet it never occurred to him that a career of electrical invention might also demand preparation.

During the month-long voyage, Morse made some preliminary sketches. The next three years he spent unsuccessfully trying to realize them in the attic of his brother Richard's home. However, in addition to his complete lack of electrical information, he had neither time nor a free mind. His wife had died, and he was responsible for three small children.

In 1834, he formulated an ambitious plan for historical paintings to fill the four remaining blank panels of the Rotunda of the National Capitol. He petitioned various members of Congress, but John Quincy Adams refused to believe that any American painter was capable of work in the style required. Morse's rejection was such a bitter disappointment that for all practical purposes he gave up painting even though he was forty-three and at the height of his power.

In the following year he got an appointment as Professor of Arts and Design at the newly established University of the City of New York, the project of culturally-minded New Yorkers like James Fenimore Cooper, Washington Irving and others. His salary was small, but he was able to live on it. He returned to his plan for an electromagnetic telegraph.

He gathered together some galvanic batteries, iron bars, and wire. He made the connections he had outlined for himself and closed the circuit. Nothing happened. He made a few more adjustments. Still nothing. For days he continued his fruitless tinkering. Finally, in desperation, he turned for help to a colleague in the chemistry department–Leonard Gale. Gale looked at Morse's pathetic contrivance and took pity on him. Morse had been told that to make an electromagnet one wound wires around a horseshoe bar of iron. Gale, who had read Joseph Henry's papers, found the windings made haphazardly, without any insulation. He showed Morse how to wind a magnet properly, and how to arrange a battery for such a circuit. By the time Gale was finished, Morse's apparatus was showing some response.

He returned to his plan for an electromagnetic telegraph

The details of Morse's early plans for a telegraph were both naive and unnecessarily complicated.

The principle was the same as Henry's: an operator opened and closed an electric circuit so that a series of current pulses were sent through a pair of wires to a receiving instrument. Later forms of the telegraph were to use a signal key, manually operated, to open and close the circuit.

Morse used only a single battery in his circuit and so he was severely limited to the length of wire over which he could send a detectable message. The longer the wire, the greater the electrical resistance. Morse, with Gale's help, progressed from twenty feet, to a hundred feet, and then to a thousand, but no further.

In September, 1837, he put on a demonstration at New York University in which he sent a message over seventeen hundred feet of wire. One of the witnesses was a prosperous ironworks owner in New Jersey, Stephen Vail, who agreed to put up

$2,000 and work space if his son Alfred could become Morse's assistant. Morse agreed, making the luckiest decision of his life. Alfred Vail had not only true inventiveness but a keen eye for practicality. Over the years that followed, Vail was largely responsible for working out the final form of Morse's code, for introducing the key, discarding the composing stick, and reducing the entire machine to the compact form that was adopted eventually. He also invented a printing telegraph that was patented in Morse's name according to his contract's terms.

He appealed to Congress for help

Shortly after meeting Vail, Morse came across the government's offer of aid to an inventor for coastwise telegraphy. In December of 1837, he appealed to Congress for help. The Chairman of the House Committee on Commerce, Francis O. J. Smith, was so impressed by Morse's demonstration that he resigned his seat and became Morse's partner. Smith was a cantankerous sharpshooter whose gift for public rhetoric and penchant for private double-dealing brought Morse trouble for the rest of his life.

The panic of 1837 put an end to any government appropriation plans. Smith rushed Morse off to Europe to secure foreign patent protection. In England, Morse was told that Wheatstone had already invented an electromagnetic telegraph as he could see for himself if he went to the nearest Post Office. On the continent, Morse was told that Steinheil had already invented an electromagnetic telegraph. Let him go to the nearest railroad station and see it.

While in France, Morse made friends with another disappointed inventor, Daguerre, who was having as much trouble trying to place his photographic process as Morse was having with telegraphy. Companions in misfortune, each agreed to act as the other's agent in his own country.

The competition for the prize

In Russia, Morse learned that Baron Schilling, the Russian Minister to Austria, had invented an electromagnetic telegraph as far back as 1825, but that the present czar considered the possibility of instantaneous communication between people at distant ends of Russia so subversive that he had banned any mention of such a thing in the press. Morse hurried back to America, broke; Mr. Smith went to Washington. None of the foreign systems were as simple as Morse's; he would not give up hope, although his situation was more desperate than ever. To augment his small income from painting he opened a small studio for taking pictures according to Daguerre's formula. This too proved a failure.

Morse's poverty during the hard years was absolute. A former painting pupil tells this story:

"Well, Strother," Morse asked one day, "how are we off for money?"

"Why, Professor, I'm sorry to say that I've been disappointed, but I expect a remittance next week."

"Next week," said Morse sadly, "I shall be dead by then."

"Dead, sir?"

"Yes, dead by starvation."

"Would ten dollars be of any service?"

"Ten dollars would save my life. That's all it would do."

The student took Morse to dinner, paid the bill and gave Morse ten dollars. Morse said: "This is my first meal in twenty-four hours. Strother, don't be an artist. It means beggary. Your life depends on people who know nothing of your art and care nothing for you. A house dog lives better."

Apparently Strother took the advice. He gave up art, entered the Army and rose to the rank of general. He led a far happier life than his teacher, but he was to be remembered only as the man who once gave ten dollars to Samuel Finley Breese Morse.

Gale had left New York to teach in the South. Morse finally took a trip to Princeton to ask Joseph Henry for advice.

Henry had no particular interest in working out the details of electromagnetic telegraphy himself. He had solved the basic problem by inventing the relay and had then gone on to far more provocative and interesting work on his own. Sooner or later, he knew, a man would come along who was sufficiently single-minded to do the job. Morse impressed him as that man.

Seeking Henry's help

Morse had sincerity and Henry was willing to help him. Patiently he explained the errors in Morse's system and pointed out that a single battery, no matter how strong, could send a signal of electrical pulses only a limited distance. The relay which Henry had developed some six years earlier was the device which would solve Morse's problem.

The sender's circuit was not connected directly to the receiver. In place of the receiver was a horseshoe of soft iron wrapped around with wire. Across the pole pieces of the iron was a movable armature. As the operator's signals opened and closed the circuit, sending pulses of current through the magnet coil, the armature, too, opened and closed. The armature, however, was actually a switch which activated a second circuit containing its own battery, its own coil, its own magnet, and operated exactly the same way as the first. In turn, this second circuit controlled a third independent circuit. In this way, an endless chain of circuits was possible. Each circuit contained its own battery and its own relay.

Henry explained to Morse that such a chain system could transmit a message of electrical pulses for thousands of miles and the signal at the end would be just as powerful as the signal originally transmitted.

Morse returned to New York and improved his system according to Henry's advice.

The government appropriation for which Morse had applied in 1837 was not finally granted until 1843, although ex-Congressman Smith's promise to him had been renewed month after month.

When the bill was finally introduced, the House thought it a huge joke, magnetism sounding something like mesmerism to the members. Morse, now a man of fifty-two, listened to the stupid humor from the gallery and then left in despair. The session was to end in the morning. There would be no time for President Tyler to sign the bill even if it were to be passed. Morse paid his boardinghouse bill and bought a ticket on the steam cars for New York, leaving him only thirty-seven cents. Next morning at breakfast, the daughter of his friend, the Commissioner of Patents, came with the fantastic news that Smith's friends had succeeded in getting through the bill shorn of all the silly amendments, and Tyler had signed it at midnight. Morse was so overjoyed that he promised her that she could send the very first message over the very first system. Her choice was to be the text, "What Hath God Wrought?"

A distance of forty miles

The terms of the government grant of thirty thousand dollars called for a test line to run between Washington and Baltimore, a distance of forty miles. Smith awarded himself the contract for construction. Morse and Vail had decided on an underground line of complicated construction within a tubular lead shield. The construction engineer, Ezra Cornell, invented a special plow that would dig a trench, unroll prepared cable, and then roll the earth back into the trench. Smith charged almost twenty thousand dollars on the first few miles. Morse was beside himself with worry. Cornell, on his own initiative, tested the line already laid and found it riddled with short circuits. Smith, it turned out, had decided not to waste valuable money on nonsense like insulation.

Cornell suggested stringing bare wires overhead as the cheapest, fastest way to get to Baltimore without precipitating a public scandal; but Morse was in a panic. Once again he ran off to Joseph Henry for advice. Henry backed Cornell, and the entire line was strung from trees and poles using broken bottle necks as insulators. The line was completed just as the Whig convention gathered in Baltimore to nominate a president. Vail was the operator in Baltimore with instructions to send to Morse in Washington the news as it broke on the floor.

Politicians coming from Baltimore with express dispatches found that their news had preceded the steam cars. A man named Morse was talking over a wire to Baltimore.

A man named Morse was talking over a wire

Morse was asked to move his wires to the Supreme Court room of the Capitol; he drew a crowd of government officials, judges and congressmen. At the high point of the Whig convention, came this exchange between Morse and Vail:

From Morse: "Have you any news?"

"No."

"Mr. Seaton's respects to you."

"My respects to him."

"What is your time?"

"Nine o'clock, twenty-eight minutes."

"What weather have you?"

"Cloudy."

"Separate your words more."

"Buchanan stock said to be rising."

"I have a great crowd here."

"Van Buren cannon in front, with foxtail on it."

Political news was interrupted occasionally with personal messages such as this one:

"As a rumor is prevalent here this morning that Mr. Eugene Boyle was shot at Baltimore last evening, Professor Morse will confer a great favor upon the family by making inquiry by means of his electromagnetic telegraph if such is the fact."

A few weeks later the Democrats also held their convention in Baltimore, and Morse sent his telegraphic dispatches to newspapers. But after that, public interest cooled. The government set aside eight thousand dollars a year to maintain the telegraph as part of the Post Office, but in 1845 the rising trouble with Mexico deflected official interest. This again was a major disappointment to Morse. Like many of his contemporaries, he was afraid of the power which the telegraph would give to a private owner to alter or withhold news and messages.

Organizing the first company

With the telegraph back in his own hands, Morse and his partner organized the Magnetic Telegraph Company for a line between New York and Philadelphia. It was to be a private stock company. At this point, Morse shut out Vail and most of his early helpers.

The real organizer of lines from the seaboard to the Mississippi was an Irish-born promoter who changed his name from O'Reilly to O'Rielly. He knew nothing about telegraphy or engineering, but he could sell stock. Each town-to-town line was a separate promotion; and like a master showman, he sent out advance scouts with the news that the *Lightning Wire* was coming. He raised money as fast as he could string wire. In less than two years, he hung thousands of miles of wire wherever he could find poles, creating more stock companies than the patent owners back East could count.

Success at last

Newspapers quickly found ways to use the telegraph, and the Associated Press set up its own wire service. By 1848 small communities were reading the latest dispatches from the Mexican War hot off the *Lightning Wire*. Before long the railroads were using the telegraph for signaling, dispatching, and traffic. Freight trains entering New York with cattle for export would wire ahead to a ship's captain, telling him how many head were coming. He then was able to arrange his deck space accordingly so that he could sail within thirty minutes of loading. For a long time all messages along the line began with "Dear Sir," and ended, "Respectfully Yours."

The early lines were constantly breaking in bad weather. In one instance, there were one hundred and seventy breaks in thirty miles of wire. First copper wire was tried and discarded for iron. Then iron was in turn dropped in favor of twisted cable. The linemen who were responsible for repairs led busy lives. Not only did they have nature to contend with, but they had to patch up after angry farmers who cut the wires because of the humming sound made by the wind.

Even worse, there was no traffic system for the various independent companies or even for individual operators. Twenty operators might be trying to send messages at once, all on the same wire.

Not until 1856, when Hiram Sibley organized the Western Union, did there begin to be any order. Then more and more lines came into existence, paying a royalty. Morse's days of poverty were over, and he spent his old age as a rich, handsomely decorated celebrity. He had fought innumerable patent suits and won them all, even though at one point he had to deny that he received much help from Joseph Henry.

The first half of the nineteenth century was hospitable only to driving, aggressive men and then only if they were driving in the direction of the material expansion of the country. When Morse gave up his early career and became an inventor, he became transformed into a man of his time. Under the same pressures, Henry steadfastly remained the kind of man he wanted most to be. Morse was satisfied with what he had become.

* * *

In the decade following Morse's first public demonstration in Washington, telegraphic networks spread across America and Europe. An inevitable step was the connection of the two continental systems by a cable on the ocean floor, even though the difficulties seemed insuperable.

The first problem was insulation. One early suggestion for insulating submarine wire was to wrap the wire tightly with layers of flannel and cotton covered with a mixture of rosin, beeswax and rubber. Other suggestions included tar and asphaltum. Submarine insulation had been solved by the use of gutta percha, a sap somewhat similar to rubber, obtained from Malaya. Gutta percha is a nonconductor which deteriorates in the sun, but retains its electrical insulating properties under water.

The next step: underwater cable

The first underwater cable insulated with gutta percha was laid successfully in 1845 between England and the Continent. In the United States, the first successful sea cable was Morse's cable between Governor's Island and Castle Garden, in 1842. Later there was a thirteen-mile line between the islands of Martha's Vineyard and Nantucket.

With the insulation problem apparently solved, three questions had to be answered:

Where was the cable to be laid?

How could messages be sent over a thousand

miles of wire without relays such as Henry's?

Who would have sufficient strength of personality to organize and oversee the infinite variety of details involved in such an undertaking?

The three questions were answered by three different men. Their joint talents were equally responsible for the greatest engineering feat of the century up to that time.

Matthew Maury was the most distinguished scientist of the American South. He had entered the United States Navy as a midshipman in 1825 and had seen active service for several years. In 1836, Maury published *A New Theoretical and Practical Treatise on Navigation for Junior Naval Officers,* and under the pen names of Henry Bluff and Will Watch, wrote blistering articles attacking the methods of educating young naval officers. As a result of the rumpus he raised, a naval academy was founded at Annapolis in 1845, similar to the Army's West Point; but Maury had made so many enemies among the senior officers that he was forced to leave active service. He was made Superintendent of the Depot of Charts and Instruments at Washington in 1842, which became the United States Naval Observatory and Hydrographical Office.

Charting the ocean currents

It was here that Maury began his great work of charting the ocean currents. On every sea voyage, American sailing masters were given blank charts which were to be filled in with daily descriptions of wind direction and velocity, compass variation, air and sea temperature, and currents.

After five years, he published *The Wind and Current Charts of the North Atlantic* which suggested lanes for sea travel insuring the fastest and safest passages. As a result of Maury's work, the average sailing time from New York to San Francisco around the Horn was cut from 180 to 133 days.

Two twenty-mile-wide ocean lanes across the Atlantic were mapped by Maury in 1855, and all American vessels were ordered to follow them. Maury had also been compiling data on the sea bottom. In 1852 he completed his topographic map of the Atlantic floor, showing for the first time the submarine mountain ranges and deeps. The map showed an underwater plateau, which Maury called the *telegraphic plateau*, between Ireland and Newfoundland.

The second question – telegraphy without relay – was answered by William Thomson, an Englishman, later famous as Lord Kelvin. His solution of the problem of dielectric loss formed the direct link between Henry's work on the oscillatory discharge of the Leyden jar and Clerk Maxwell's fourth equation of electrodynamics.

Cyrus Field: organizing genius

The third need – an organizing genius – was supplied by an American, Cyrus W. Field – a retired paper merchant who, at thirty-five, looked forward to a life of ease, entirely unaware that he was to be swept up into an enterprise that would make him risk his fortune, his sanity, and his integrity in a test that was to go on for twelve years.

The project of a cable from the United States to Newfoundland was broached to Field in 1854. The colossal scale of the undertaking appealed to him. He consulted Morse, who had no idea of the difficulties involved; and Morse gave him easy approval. Field then sounded out several New York businessmen. They agreed to go along.

The New York, Newfoundland and London Electric Telegraph Company was organized in May, 1854, with a capital of $1,500,000. Cyrus Field went to England to buy cable. His brother, the company's engineer, went to Newfoundland to start land construction. The cable for the first leg of fifty-five miles to Newfoundland arrived from England in the summer of 1855, and the laying of the line began immediately.

The steamer, *James Adger,* was to tow the cable-carrying bark, *Sarah Bryant*. Bad weather delayed a start for several days, then strong winds arose and the towline parted. Next morning a new start was made. The cable was spliced; and after a run of a few miles, the *Adger* was sent off course by currents. Another gale made up, leaving both vessels wallowing helplessly. To save themselves, they had to cut loose forty miles of underwater cable.

The first step—the attempt to lay a short line to Newfoundland—was a failure. The following summer, more capital was raised and the connection from the mainland to Newfoundland was successfully made. The cost to date was over a million dollars and only the smallest step had been taken.

The attempt to bridge the Atlantic with wire

Field went to England again and organized the Atlantic Telegraph Company of Great Britain, which absorbed the original American company and raised close to two million dollars. The British government promised vessels to help lay the cable and asked for favored use of the cable on its completion. Field fought a bill through Congress getting him similar support. For cable laying, the United States Navy detached its largest vessel, the *Niagara,* and sent along the *Susquehanna* as its tender. The Royal Navy assigned the *Agamemnon* and the *Leopard* to the same task. The four vessels met on the coast of Ireland in Valentia Bay on August 14.

The shore end of the cable was fixed, speeches were made, and the flotilla sailed, paying cable as it went. Constant communication was maintained between the ships and Thomson at the shore end.

Four days out, 360 miles had been laid to a depth of two miles, and the cable was transmitting. At nine o'clock that evening, signal strength flickered, vanished, and then returned. At 3:45 in the morning, miles below the surface, a fraction of an inch of copper failed, and the great cable was parted. With flags at half-mast, the flotilla steamed back to Valentia Bay. The cost was a half million dollars.

The following summer Field had a new plan of action. In June, 1858, the flotilla made a rendezvous in midocean, each carrying half the cable. The *Niagara* and the *Agamemnon* spliced ends and then sailed off in opposite directions, the *Niagara* towards America, the *Agamemnon* east to Ireland. After three miles, the *Niagara's* end was fouled. A new splice was made, and this time forty miles were laid before signals stopped. After a third start, two hundred miles of cable were paid out. A break then occurred on the *Agamemnon*.

The ships' captains returned to Ireland and advised the Board of Directors that the whole thing was impractical. Only Field's impassioned optimism convinced the board to make another try. On June 17, the cable fleet left Ireland with Field aboard the *Niagara*. Two weeks later, the ships arrived at midocean, spliced cable ends and began again. The weather was good. Both vessels continually reported to each other with absolute clarity. One week later, at seven o'clock in the morning, the lookout on the *Niagara* called "Land Ho!" At two-thirty in the afternoon the American vessels entered Trinity Bay, Newfoundland, just as the receiver was bringing the news that the *Agamemnon* had raised the Irish shore. At eight o'clock that night, August 8, 1858, Cyrus Field went ashore, walked fifteen miles to the nearest telegraph station, reaching it at two-thirty in the morning. He sent wires to Mrs. Field, the Associated Press, and to President Buchanan, telling him that Queen Victoria would greet him just as soon as

A glorious new era had arrived

the two ends of the cable were connected with land networks.

Before the cable was laid, the company's stock was selling at three hundred dollars. It rose immediately to a thousand. The public reaction after years of skepticism was one of hysterical jubilation. Spontaneous celebrations broke out all over the country. Poems were written, songs composed, and Longfellow's diary says: "August 6th – Go to town with the boys. Flags flying and bells ringing to celebrate the laying of the telegraph." In New York, celebrations awaited the Queen's message.

All through America, there was the conviction that a glorious new era had arrived for men, that instant communication between the old world and the new would put an end to all strife and misunderstanding. There would be peace – *peace – peace!*

In the meantime, the two operators at opposite ends of the cable were the only ones who were aware that something was dying even before it was born. Eleven days of night and day adjustment passed and finally the Queen's message began to arrive at 4:15 in the afternoon. Two hours of constant repetition were required to get through the following sentence. "The Queen desires to congratulate the President upon the successful completion of the great international work, in which the Queen has taken the greatest interest."

A pandemonium of church bells and whistles

The rest of the message was not completed for another twelve hours, but impatient celebrants did not bother to wait. In New York a pandemonium of church bells, factory whistles, fireworks, gun reports tore the town apart. The city was festooned with banners, and banquets were held. As a final touch of joy, the City Hall was set afire.

Disappointment was so bitter when the cable finally went dead that most people began to doubt that the cable had ever worked at all. It had been too good to be true.

For weeks, both operators worked sleeplessly trying to re-establish communication, but the silence was unbroken. Months later it was reported that the fault was due to insulation. When the wire was being made, careless workmen had left coil after coil of the gutta-percha-covered cable exposed in the sun, against all instructions.

Approaching a moment of triumph

All during the war, Field kept pushing away at his project. In July, 1865, with the *Great Eastern,* the largest steamboat afloat and now adapted for cable-laying, another attempt was made. The great vessel and three tenders left Valentia harbor with ceremonies as joyous as on the first occasion. Communication with the shore was kept up all the time. There were failures; but on each occurrence the huge steamer retraced its path, hauling in cable until the faulty section was found and mended. When the *Great Eastern* was only 660 miles from Newfoundland, after maintaining perfect communication with Ireland, the cable parted. For almost two weeks the *Great Eastern* cruised back and forth over the ocean, finding and losing the cable, trying to raise it with inadequate hoisting tackle. Finally a buoy was thrown over to mark the spot. It was a time of the greatest despair, and even the indomitable Field broke down and wept like a child.

Still Field refused to give up. The following year, 1866, a new corporation was formed, the Anglo-American Company, which absorbed all the previous companies. Once again, the *Great Eastern* sailed from Ireland with almost 2,500 miles of cable in her hold. But this time every flaw of past technique was known. Within ten days, the *Great Eastern* was steaming past the spot where the 1865 cable was lost, and cable was still being paid out. Field cabled to London, "We are within 400 miles of Heart's Content. Expect to be there Friday. When shall Atlantic cable be opened for public business?" London replied, "If you land Friday, open Saturday."

At seven o'clock Friday morning, July 27, Heart's Content came into sight and at 8:55 Cyrus Field went ashore. He personally telegraphed the news of the safe landing. Then without any delay, but to everyone's surprise, he returned aboard the *Great Eastern* and steamed back out to sea.

At that moment of triumph, his disappearance seemed inexplicable, but Field was fulfilling a promise to himself. The *Great Eastern* was returning to the spot where the cable had been lost the previous year. Back and forth over the empty ocean she cruised, feeling the bottom with new grappling apparatus. The lost end of the 1865 cable was actually found and raised, and on being tested, proved to be in perfect condition. With new wire spliced to the old cable, the *Great Eastern* then returned to Newfoundland and the second wire was landed, working flawlessly. The recapture of the old cable caught the world's imagination far more than the first successful completion and Field was vindicated.

* * *

A tribute to Professor Morse

Toward the close of 1868 his fellow-citizens invited Morse to meet them at a public dinner. The letter of invitation was addressed to him by a large number of distinguished gentlemen, who united in saying:

"Many of your countrymen, and numerous personal friends, desire to give a definite expression of the fact that this country is in full accord with European nations in acknowledging your title to the position of the Father of the Modern Telegraphs, and at the same time, in a fitting manner, to welcome you to your home."

The invitation was accepted, and the day designated for the banquet was December 30, 1868. It was designed as the crowning honor of the great inventor's life, by his own countrymen.

As the venerable Professor arose to respond, the whole audience broke into a warm cheer of salutation. His long white beard falling on his breast, his erect and graceful form, and his evident emotion, commanded the admiring sympathy of the audience. After a few words of introduction, while struggling to control his emotions, he said:

"In the carrying out of any plan of improvement, however grand or feasible, no single individual could possibly accomplish it without the aid of others. We are, none of us, so powerful that we can dispense with the assistance, in various departments of the work, of those whose experience and knowledge must supply the needed aid of their expertness. It is not sufficient that a brilliant project be proposed, that its modes of accomplishment are foreseen and properly devised; there are, in every part of the enterprise, other minds, and other agencies to be consulted for information and counsel to protect the whole plan. The Chief Justice, in delivering the decision of the Supreme Court, says: 'It can make no difference whether he' (the inventor) 'derives his information from books or from conversation with men skilled in the science'–and 'the fact that Morse sought and obtained the necessary information and counsel from the best sources, and acted upon it, neither impairs his rights as an inventor nor detracts from his merits.' The inventor must seek and employ the skilled mechanician in his workshop, to put the invention into practical form, and for this purpose some pecuniary means are required, as well as mechanical skill. Both these were at hand.

What hath God wrought!

"When I consider that he who rules supreme over the ways and destinies of man often makes use of the feeblest instruments to accomplish his benevolent purposes to man, as if, by grandest contrast, to point the mind with more marked effect to him as their author, I cheerfully take my place on the lowest seat at his footstool. It is his pleasure, however, to work by human instrumentality. You have chosen to impersonate, in the statue this day, erected the invention rather than the inventor, and it is of no small significance that in the attitude so well chosen, and so admirably executed by the talented young sculptor whose work presents him so prominently and so favorably before you, he has given permanence to that pregnant and just sentence which was the first public utterance of the telegraph: 'What hath God wrought!'"

Innovation & Achievement

1845

Elias Howe Jr

5

They asked me if my machine could compete in a demonstration with five of their best seamstresses. It did and the work was declared to be superior.

By the 1830s the republic was half a century old, and half a continent wide. The time was beginning to pass when every farm household produced all its own necessities. The cities were growing rapidly and city dwellers earned cash wages to buy the articles their parents and grandparents had made at home.

To supply the wants of the town, factories had to turn out large quantities of goods. In 1831, although most women still made their own dresses and their husbands went to tailors, George Opdyke started the first ready-to-wear clothing factory in America. All the work was done by hand. Other such factories sprang up and seamstresses and tailors were kept busy because the demand was enormous. The American market was ready for a machine that could sew.

The American market was ready for a machine that could sew

The first sewing machine on record was the 1790 conception of Thomas Saint, an Englishman. His machine was designed to sew leather. Although his plans were completed, no machine was ever built. It was forgotten and the records lost for almost a hundred years. However, the economic need for such a device was increasingly obvious, and so the sewing machine was reinvented over and over, independently, by a number of other men.

Others had tried and failed

In the late 1820s a French tailor named Barthelemy Thimonnier invented a sewing machine which produced a chain stitch by means of a crochet type of needle. The chain stitch had the disadvantage that when the thread was broken in any one place the entire seam unraveled. Nevertheless, Thimonnier's machine was so much faster than handwork that once he received his patent, in 1830, he had no trouble finding buyers. Eighty sewing machines were employed in making uniforms for the French Army in 1831, and Thimonnier immediately prospered. In France, however, the early 1830s produced the same revolutionary spirit which, in the United States, had elected Jackson. Mistakenly, political repression was identified with the introduction of labor saving devices, and a mob of tailors raided Thimonnier's shop, smashed every machine and threatened the inventor's life. He fled and made a living by selling handmade wooden machines at ten dollars apiece. In 1848 he had an improved machine that was in factory work once more, but the Revolution destroyed everything he had. Thimonnier was defeated not by lack of ingenuity, inventiveness or persistence, but by the time and the place in which he lived.

At about the same time as Thimonnier was working in France, one of the most brilliant, versatile and unworldly inventors in American history was developing the same idea in New York.

Walter Hunt, between the years of 1832 and 1859, invented and developed a greater number and variety of original ideas than anyone else. Among them: machinery for making nails and rivets, ice plows, a sea camel (a small floating drydock), velocipedes, the paper collar, a revolver, a repeating rifle, a bullet with a metal cartridge containing its own explosive charge, and the safety pin.

The safety pin was invented in three hours one afternoon to discharge a debt of fifteen dollars which Hunt owed to J. R. Chapin, a draftsman. Chapin paid four hundred dollars for all rights to the various forms in which Hunt twisted an old piece of wire. Hunt's ideas came so fast that he had no time to make more than a passing show of getting himself legal protection.

After carrying the idea for a sewing machine around in his head for several years, in 1832 he set to work in a shop on Amos Street in New York and built a machine "for sewing, stitching, and seaming cloth." Hunt's machine could sew only a straight seam; the work could not be turned and the seam was only a few inches long.

The basic needs of a sewing machine are: a needle that will carry the thread through the material and out again, forming a complete stitch; a means of advancing the work after each stitch; and a source of power to drive the needle and advance the work. Hunt's machine had an inadequate feed. His basic invention was a needle with an eye in its point. The needle moved in a straight line like a piston's rise and fall. It was driven through the two pieces of cloth, momentarily leaving a loop of thread underneath the work. Through this loop, a small shuttle carried another thread. On the needle's upward stroke, the two locked threads were pulled taut forming a *lock stitch* which would not unravel when the thread was broken in any one place.

Labor-saving devices were considered immoral

Hunt urged his daughter Caroline to employ the new invention and go into the business of manufacturing corsets. This was 1838 and one of the new trends of American thought, as in France, was the belief that machinery displaced the laboring classes and was therefore immoral. Both felt that too many seamstresses would be thrown out of work. Rather than injure society, Hunt withdrew his machine. He never applied for the patent.

In the very same year that Hunt in New York shelved his machine, an undersized, young apprentice in Boston overheard an argument between his employer, Ari Davis, a model builder, and a customer who had come to ask about a knitting machine.

"What are you bothering with a knitting machine for?" Davis screamed. "Why don't you make a sewing machine?"

"Can't be done," said the customer.

"I can make a sewing machine," Davis said.

"Well, you do it, Davis, and I'll assure you an independent fortune."

The argument ended there and Davis forgot his boast. The apprentice, who was in desperate need of any kind of fortune, independent or otherwise, paid attention to what he had heard.

* * *

Bleak New England farms produce inventors

Bleak New England farms do not as a rule raise bumper crops, but they certainly seem to produce inventors who have the necessary iron will implanted in them to stick to their work until it is done and get the full value of it. It did not take the New Englanders long, after they had rid themselves of hostile Indians, to find that they must use all their ingenuity to wrest a living out of their rock-strewn acres.

The father of Elias Howe, Jr., owned one of these barren farms near Spencer, Massachusetts, and there in 1819 the inventor of the sewing machine was born. The elder Howe eked out his income by running a small gristmill; he also manufactured cards for the growing cotton industry of New England. Among the earliest recollections of the long-haired, high-cheek-boned, and puny Elias Howe was that of bending over a bench and putting bits of wire on the wooden forms which made up the comb-like contrivance known as a card, with which the fibers of the cotton were pulled. At six years of age, Elias worked with his brothers and sisters at stitching wire teeth into cards for cotton mills. Later on he attended the village school in winter, and in summer took a hand in farm work and his father's mills. Day by day this observing boy saw what machinery did to lighten toil and multiply its fruit. And, besides this, he received a cultivation of hand and eye, of good sense and resourcefulness, which made his training, unsystematic though it was, a capital preparation for his labors as an inventor. One day he trued a grindstone, glazed a window, and soldered a teakettle, next morning he nailed shingles on a leaky roof; the week afterward saw him building a corn crib, rearing a well sweep, and bringing from the wood lot a new prop for his mother's clothesline.

Elias Howe and his start

And meantime he was acquiring, too, more than mere handiness; he received the sterling discipline of sticking to a task, whether he liked it or not, until that task was finished. From boyhood, as long as he lived, Elias Howe had the unrelaxing grip of a bulldog; when once his mind was made up, he was deaf to dissuasion and proof against discouragement. He had other traits which smoothed his path for purposes firmly maintained. As a boy he was lively and play-loving, with chums aplenty. As a man he was kind and sociable, so that, in his darkest days, he never lacked a friend to proffer him aid and comfort.

In his twelfth year he went to live with a farmer in the neighborhood, intending to remain with him until he had thoroughly mastered the routine of planting, tilling, and reaping. But young Howe suffered from a lameness which, though slight, was disabling; this made farm drudgery a distress to him, so that, within a year, he returned home to resume work in his father's mills. This continued until he was sixteen. (At that critical age, with new ambition astir, a friend told him how bright and busy a place Lowell was, where Elias could earn much more than at Spencer, and have a much better time.) So to Lowell he went, taking a learner's place in a large factory of cotton machinery. Here he remained for two years, when the panic of 1837 closed every mill in town and sent him adrift. He went to Cambridge, and there found work in a machine shop, taking charge of a hemp-carder invented by Professor Treadwell, of Harvard College. (As a shopmate and roommate, Howe had his cousin, Nathaniel P. Banks, who became a Major General of the United States Army, and Speaker of the House of Representatives.) After a few months of hemp-carding, a task not to his mind, Howe heard of pleasant work in Boston at better wages.

A fateful trip to Boston

There he came in contact with Ari Davis, a maker of mariners' instruments and scientific apparatus, and a rough hewer of men's destinies. Howe was eighteen years old at this time and his meeting with Davis meant much to him. He learned to develop his ideas and how to get at the root of the difficulty without wasting too much time. It is likely that Howe, without knowing it, picked up many of the mannerisms of Davis. Many inventors are off in their ways, but Davis was queer even for an inventor. He was often asked to make apparatus for the professors of Harvard University, and he could turn out a model of the solar system or rig up an air pump and keep up two or three conversations at the same time. Inventors often went to Ari Davis to ask his advice about models they had made, which were good enough in their way except that they would not work. Sometimes he helped them, and sometimes he shouted at them in anger, for he was one of the noisiest men in Boston. His clothes, too, were characteristically loud and unusual, for Davis prided himself on wearing the most outlandish, voluminous, and gaily colored garments.

It was there that young Howe chanced one day to hear the fateful challenge. The man with the money thought that the machine might be developed, if it would only work, and wished to retain Davis as a consulting expert.

Davis, like most men of many words, was short on performance, and he never did invent a sewing machine. In fact, he probably thought no more of the suggestion; but the keen witted boy of eighteen who was standing by his side could not forget that sentence, "I can make a sewing machine myself," and the promise of the capitalist. And from that moment began the career of Elias Howe.

Howe married when he was twenty years old, just when his work on the sewing machine was beginning. All too frequently young Howes came into this world, to share the haps and the mishaps of their father's lot. The inventor's health was often so poor that he had to stop work for days at a time and sit about the house with a wet bandage on his head, trying to get over his numerous headaches. Things went so badly that Mrs. Howe took in sewing, and while the inventor saw before him the vision of the machine that would release her precious fingers from toil, he was forced to realize that his idea was, as yet, merely a dream, and that what his wife was doing was the grim reality.

But Elias Howe, grim prophet of an age of power, possessed a heart of steel. Year after year he worked on at his trade of machinist, earning just enough to enable him to get food for his family, while he spent all his spare time in perfecting his invention.

The struggle for the goal

Tinkering away in his small home shop, he must have presented a strange sight. Working away at his model, his long and shaggy hair falling in waves from his puckered forehead, his clothes shabby, his form became bent by close attention to his yet unrewarded toil. Despite the complaints of his family and the chidings of his friends, who thought he was a poor lunatic and an idle dreamer, he persevered.

Like some of his fellow workers, Howe at first fell into the mistake of trying to follow too exactly the motions of the human hand and arm in sewing. The truth is that a machine which mimics such motions must always analyze those motions and then create or restore them in the finished work. The binder which is part of a reaping machine, for instance, seems to be doing just what the human hand does in tying a knot in the twine that holds together a sheaf of wheat; but in reality it is doing that magic task with the equivalent of three fingers. The early inventors of the airplanes believed that the so-called wings really had to flop up and down, as do the wings of a bird; but they discovered that the canvas wings need only be supports and the propellers would do the work of sending the flying craft through the air. For many years Howe had been working out in his mind a great principle without having had the benefit of the successes and failures of other inventors, for he knew little or nothing about their work.

In continuing to imitate the motions of his wife's all too busy needle, Howe made the needles of his early failures with a hole in the middle of the shank. His brain was busy with the invention day and night and even when he slept. One night he dreamed, so the story goes, that he was captured by a tribe of savages who took him a prisoner before their king.

"Elias Howe," roared the monarch, "I command you on pain of death to finish this machine at once."

Cold sweat poured down his brow, his hands shook with fear, his knees quaked. Try as he would, the inventor could not get the missing figure in the problem over which he had worked so long. All this was so real to him that he cried aloud. In the vision he saw himself surrounded by dark-skinned and painted warriors, who formed a hollow square about him and led him to the place of execution. Suddenly he noticed that near the heads of the spears which his guards carried, there were eye-shaped holes! He had solved the secret! What he needed was a needle with an eye near the point! He awoke from his dream, sprang out of bed, and at once made a whittled model of the eye-pointed needle, with which he brought his experiments to a successful close. As we have seen, Hunt had invented the eye-pointed needle, wide-awake in broad daylight and not in a dream. Much was made of this in patent suits in which Howe was later involved, but Hunt never took the trouble to patent his great idea.

Eureka! The answer in a dream

Scant as were his funds, Howe did a great deal in the months which followed his vision. Most of the work was done in the attic of a factory for splitting palm leaves which his father had started at Cambridge. When this building burned down, Howe was for days in the depths of despair until he thought of his old schoolmate, George Fisher, who had received a small inheritance. Like many another man who has had a windfall of good fortune, Fisher was willing to let some easily gained money go in backing what he considered at most a very risky venture. He lent $500 to Howe and entered into one of the strangest partnerships in the history of invention.

A very risky venture

For an interest in the invention Fisher was to take Howe and his numerous family into his house, there to feed and lodge them, and also give the attic of the dwelling over to the inventor for a workshop.

In building the second machine, Howe spent all the money advanced by Fisher. The machine was ready in May 1845, but was not patented until the following September. Howe rested a little on his oars then, for he believed that at the age of twenty-six he had won his long pull against the tide. He set up his machine in a public hall in Boston, and after much cajoling he induced a tailor to operate it for about three times the usual wage. Howe's reception by the regular garment makers was similar to that suffered by the unfortunate Thimonnier. A gaping crowd went to see the "new-fangled contraption," but when Howe tried to get the big clothing establishments to use the machine he found out exactly where he stood; the howl of the tailors echoed to the Bunker Hill Monument.

Two months later, in July 1845, he sewed all the seams on two woolen suits. That summer, too, he arranged with the Quincy Hall Clothing Manufacturing Company in Boston for a demonstration in which he would sew in competition with five of the best seamstresses. Howe's machine finished his five seams a little sooner than the five girls finished theirs and his work was declared to be superior. The owners, though, bought no machines.

Enthusiasm, but no sale

"This," said the manufacturer, after he had seen the machine demonstrated, "is the beginning of a tremendous enterprise. And the man who has carried it thus far is the man to carry it farther."

On September 10, 1846, Howe received his patent. At this point, Fisher, who had laid out some two thousand dollars, lost interest. Elias Howe's brother, Amasa, took one of the machines to England where he finally interested William Thomas, manufacturer of corsets, umbrellas, valises and shoes. He paid fifteen hundred dollars for the English rights to the machine and agreed to give Howe a royalty on every machine that was sold except those he used himself. Moreover, he insisted that Howe come to England to perfect a leather sewing machine in his factory. On February 5, 1847, the Howe brothers set sail. Elias Howe's wife and three children followed.

But poor Howe's troubles were not over yet. William Thomas certainly bought a machine from him for 250 pounds—about 1,250 dollars—and with it he acquired the entire rights of the new sewing machine for Great Britain. Howe was retained by the Thomas establishment at a salary of fifteen dollars a week, and this kept him from begging his bread. He was to adapt his invention for the sewing of heavy leather, used in traveling bags and other articles, in the making of which the English have always excelled. But after eight months or so, a quarrel arose and amicable relations between employer and inventor came to an end. Poor Howe was again without a job.

He took this ill turn with good grace, and started to build another machine. His funds ran so low, however, that he was obliged to take his family to cheaper lodgings. Things went from bad to worse.

Things went from bad to worse

He borrowed money to send his family home; then pawned his machine and patent papers to pay for his own passage. To feed himself, he acted as cook for his fellow steerage passengers. He arrived in New York in April 1849, penniless, and looked for work in the machine shops. Word reached him that his wife was dying of consumption in Cambridge and he had to borrow $10 from his father to get to her bedside before she died. Howe's whole outlook changed. Until now, he had been gay and indomitably hopeful. After his wife's death he became quiet and bitter – full of a sense of outrage.

While he was in England, his sewing machine had begun to be adopted in the United States. The money due him from royalties would certainly have saved his wife's life. Also, Thomas had been manufacturing his machine in England without royalties. Howe was determined to fight the infringers not only to protect himself, but out of anger that his wife had been so needlessly deprived. His old partner, Fisher, had sold his interest to George W. Bliss, who advanced the money needed to carry on the suit. As security, Bliss demanded and got a mortgage on the farm of Howe's father. Howe went to court and relentlessly fought all infringers with a determination born of his bitterness. He was sustained in every court, though his opposition was powerful.

One of the longest lawsuits in the history of patent law

The rights of Howe were not fully established in the courts until 1854, and the fight for them was one of the longest in the history of American patent law. Many thousands of pages of testimony were taken which are in themselves a record of sewing machine invention. With the proceeds of one or two successful suits, Howe was able to provide himself still further with the sinews of war. He was a rather gaunt and fierce figure in those days, for the death of a wife who missed sharing his good fortune had added to his firm resolve to get all that he could for the product of his brains. His patent was declared basic, and the courts gave him judgment for a twenty-five-dollar royalty on every sewing machine built that infringed his patent. It was success at last. But Howe must have been haunted by the vision of the deathbed of one who shared all his sorrows and none of his joys.

During the life of his patent, fourteen years, Howe's income often reached $4,000 a week. He held that his rights were really worth as much as $150,000,000, and when, in 1860, he petitioned Congress for a further extension, he stated that up to that date he had received only $1,185,000. Although Howe had invented, demonstrated, and sold his machines, he never had a factory of his own. The one at Bridgeport, Connecticut, popularly believed to be owned by him, belonged to his brother, Amasa Howe. It was the center of many lawsuits, brought by other inventors who declared that, although the machines built there were nominally made on the Howe principles, their own ideas had also been embodied in them.

He never had a factory of his own

Elias Howe again showed his mettle in the Civil War. He enlisted as a private soldier in a Connecticut regiment which he organized. Elected colonel by the men, he refused a commission and served in the ranks, although placing his means at the regiment's disposal. Once he advanced the money for the entire payroll, taking his own $13.60 with his comrades when the cash was paid. He died in Brooklyn in 1867, only two years after the struggle between the North and South had come to a close.

The excitement caused by the many suits of Howe against his competitors stimulated the invention of sewing machines of all kinds, and there are now more than a thousand patents for such devices in our national archives.

After Howe's victory, he was approached by a combination of manufacturers who agreed to all his terms, and the sewing machine pool headed by Isaac Singer was on its way to fantastic wealth.

The invention created new industries and a better way of life for the multitudes

The sewing machine was one of the first inventions, typical of America, to make living easier and more comfortable. The sewing machine not only appeared in every home, but found innumerable uses in American factories.

Innovation & Achievement

1875

Alexander Graham Bell

6

Watson, what did you do then? Don't change anything. Let me see!

The conquest of solitude

Through an accident on a warm June afternoon in 1875, Bell discovered the means to make his telephone. He and Watson had been working on the harmonic telegraph. The receiver and the transmitter were in two different rooms. Both consisted of a number of springlike metal strips that were clamped only at one end. The strips were of different lengths, so that each one would vibrate at a different musical note. Watson, at the transmitter, was having trouble with one metal reed whose free end had become stuck. As he worked on it, he kept touching the other reeds, which set up a jangling noise. Although the line was supposed to be dead, Bell's very acute hearing picked up the faint jangling sound at the receiver. He immediately guessed what was happening and ran into Watson's room.

"What did you do then?" he exclaimed. "Don't change anything. Let me see!"

Watson started to explain his trouble, but Bell excitedly pointed out that they had found exactly what they had been working for all along. The stuck reed was working like a primitive diaphragm. The conventional method of operation had been for the vibrating free end of the reed to make and break an electrical contact; instead, its slight movement was now *inducing* its own vibrations in the electromagnet directly behind it.

This was the difference between the telephone and every other telegraphic device that had preceded it. Telegraphy transmitted sharply defined *pulses* of current, each pulse having the same intensity, even though the current pulse for a *dash* was longer than for a *dot*. A telephone required a *continuous current* whose intensity could *vary* exactly as the sound waves in the air.

An electrician could have known every facet of circuit behavior, but only an acoustician would have been aware of the exact nature of the continuously varying current required for telephony.

That night Bell gave Watson directions for the first true electric speaking telephone: a tiny drumhead whose center was to be adapted to one of the springs. To concentrate the sound, a small flaring horn was mounted over the drumhead. Within a very short time, Watson completed Bell's apparatus, and it worked, although very feebly.

This was essentially the form of the telephone for which Bell made his patent application. It was granted March 7, 1876, only a few months before the Centennial.

* * *

One August morning in 1906, at his summer retreat in Nova Scotia, Alexander Graham Bell was roused from a dream about kites – his latest scientific preoccupation – with the news that a grandson had been born. Still half asleep, Bell asked: "Can it fly?"

What sort of man was this? One who combined a soaring imagination with an insatiable need to know (Bell's son-in-law, David Fairchild, once said "Wondering to him was almost a passion.") Together with a bulldog persistence, these qualities shaped an extraordinarily successful, multifaceted career.

Bell was one of the most idolized men of his time, a world traveler, society lion, and hobnobber with the great. The invention of the telephone alone would have assured him all this. But there was much, much more. A list of the things Bell invented or helped develop is wonderfully varied: a hydrofoil boat that held the world's speed record for ten years; a phonograph; a "vacuum jacket" that was the precursor of the iron lung; air conditioning; a telephonic bullet probe; scientific sheep breeding; the audiometer; a light-beam telephone; man-carrying kites; an airplane.

An abundant and rewarding contribution to mankind

And his activities outside the realm of invention were both abundant and rewarding to his fellowman. He helped establish *Science* magazine; was the second president of the National Geographic Society and launched its successful magazine; and was a regent of the Smithsonian Institution. He was an early sponsor of the Montessori method of early childhood education in this country. And throughout his life, he was a gifted speech teacher, devoted to the problems of the deaf. (Whenever he was asked to list his occupation, the father of the telephone answered, "teacher of the deaf.") Toward this goal, he gave some half million dollars in charity.

All in all, one might think, enough to satisfy any man – even a titan. But the great irony of Bell's long and singular life is that for most of it he was haunted by a baseless fear; that his supreme achievement, the telephone, had come so early (at age twenty-nine) it would rob the rest of his work of real meaning. "I can't bear to hear," he wrote in 1879, "that even my friends should think I stumbled upon an invention and there is no more good in me." For

Bell, if fame could not be the spur, fear was.

Alexander Bell (he gave himself the middle name of Graham on his eleventh birthday) was born in Edinburgh, Scotland, on March 3, 1847 . . . the same year as Edison. Aleck was named after two previous Bells, prophetically, for rarely has a great man's lineage been so visible in his own life.

Scottish beginnings

Aleck's was a family of Scottish speech specialists and actors. His grandfather, the first Alexander Bell, was a stage comedian, then prospered giving speech and elocution lessons. He published a book on stammering, and one called *The Practical Elocutionist* that used symbols to show phrasing and stress. By the time he was forty-eight, an account of one of his public recitations referred to him as "the celebrated Professor of Elocution."

One of Grandfather Bell's sons was David Charles Bell, who became a teacher of speech and a Shakespearean actor. Aleck's uncle David struck a young George Bernard Shaw as being "by far the most majestic and impressive looking man that ever lived on this or any other planet." (All the Bell men seemed to have had compelling physical appearance, magnetic personal presence, and magnificent voice.)

Aleck's own father, Alexander Melville Bell, was an internationally known teacher of speech and elocution, a phonetician who invented "Visible Speech." This was an influential pioneer system for representing, on paper, any speech sound in any language, using symbols for the placement and movement of throat, tongue, and lips. Alexander Melville may even have inspired the character in Shaw's *Pygmalion* who transmutes base cockney into noble English – Professor Henry Higgins.

Aleck's mother, née Eliza Grace Symonds, was the daughter of a naval surgeon. A painter of miniatures, living with her widowed mother in Edinburgh, she was thirty-four when she met Alexander Melville Bell in 1843, ten years older than he. And she was already quite deaf, relying on an ear tube to hear at all. Remarkably, she was also a talented pianist; she could monitor her playing only by using the mouthpiece of her ear tube to pick up vibrations from the piano's sounding board. In outlook, she was much different from Aleck's father – deeply religious and observant where he was careless of the strict Scottish Sabbath rules and somewhat skeptical – but their marriage seems to have been blissfully calm. After she died in 1897, Alexander Melville Bell wrote: "She was so kind, so gentle, so loving, that during the fifty-two years of our companionship, I never saw a frown on her sweet face."

In his early childhood, at least, Aleck's predilections and talents seemed strongly molded by his mother. He was a pious little boy, even taking his father to task for not being sufficiently reflective on Sundays. He became so adept musically that his mother retained a well-known pianist, Auguste Benoit Bertini, to give him lessons. For a while, both master and pupil dreamed of a great concert career. Aleck eventually went other ways, but never lost his love for the piano.

Like so many other brilliant men, Aleck had a lackluster record in school. With his older brother Melly (Melville James) and his younger brother Ted (Edward Charles) he attended the Royal High School. He hated Latin and Greek, was stultified by the rote work in mathematics, and never ventured to take any science courses at all. Outside school, however, Aleck was developing a lively interest in the natural world. He collected plants (but strongly resisted labeling them with their correct Latin names). He dissected animals. He learned to prepare and develop the clumsy glass photographic plates of the day. And, around age fourteen, he produced his first real invention, at the instigation of a friend's father, who owned a flour mill called, coincidentally, Bell's Mill. The problem was to remove the husks from wheat before it was ground. When Aleck found that a stiff-bristled nail brush would do the job, and remembered seeing a device at the mill that used rotating paddles, he melded the two ideas, suggesting a rotary brushing wheel. His friend's father had one built, and it worked so well he used it happily for years.

The turning point

In 1862, the fifteen-year-old inventor made a move that he later described as "the turning point of my life." Leaving school after only four years instead of the full six-year curriculum (would it be merely facetious to call him a Royal High School dropout?), he joined his grandfather in London. Alexander Bell, seventy-two, was still teaching speech and elocution, a practice he immediately extended to young Aleck, whose declamatory gifts he burnished with joint readings from Shakespeare. He insisted also on transforming the adolescent's dress. Soon Aleck was turned out in full London gentleman's regalia, including kid gloves, top hat, and cane. Though he chafed somewhat at the restrictions of town life in London, his exposure to the magnificent old man gave him a new sense of independence and a seriousness of purpose he had never felt before. When he returned home after a year's visit, he had been "converted . . . from a boy somewhat prematurely into a man."

Before the trip back to Edinburgh, Aleck was taken by his father to the London workshop of the eminent electrical experimenter Sir Charles Wheatstone. Years before, Wheatstone had made his own contribution to the centuries-old effort to produce a "speaking machine"–a mechanical device that could mimic the human voice–and it was this that had led Alexander Melville Bell to his door. Wheatstone trotted out his venerable model, an improvement over an eighteenth-century design, and it dutifully though creakily delivered a few simple words and sentences. Once home, Aleck and Melly together built their own "speaking machine" by duplicating the human vocal apparatus out of assorted materials. Modeling their organs carefully from real ones, they assembled a tin tube throat; a rubber larynx; gutta-percha jaws, teeth, pharynx, and nasal cavities; rubber lips and cheeks; a rubber palate stuffed with cotton; and, most ingenious of all, a wooden, rubber-covered tongue in six segments that could be raised and lowered individually by levers, so as to shape and position the whole tongue naturally. For lungs, the boys relied on their own.

Through trial and error, Aleck learned how to adjust tongue, lips, and palate to get the desired sounds. Shakespeare was well beyond the machine's capacity. But its wailing "mama" was so lifelike that a neighbor solicitously inquired after "the baby's" welfare. The whole endeavor was an ideal one for a novice inventor to chew on. Moreover, it gave Aleck a sound and permanent grounding in the mechanics of speech production.

Intoxication with the spoken word

Clearly, it seemed, Aleck was to pursue the family intoxication with the spoken word. In 1863, a stately sixteen, he took a one-year job as teacher of elocution and music at Weston House, a boarding school for "young gentlemen" at Elgin on the northern coast of Scotland, and was a considerable success there. Returning from Elgin in the summer of 1864, he was plunged, with his brothers, into demonstrations of his father's revolutionary phonetic alphabet, "Visible Speech," which had finally been finished after a quarter-century's effort.

He took classes at the University of Edinburgh, returned to Weston House as an assistant master, and pursued his own researches into the puzzles of speech, investigating the exact pitch of vowel sounds with the aid of tuning forks set resonating in front of his mouth. When Aleck reported on his work to Alexander Ellis, a noted phonetician, Ellis told him that he was in fact independently duplicating an identical set of experiments that had been carried out by the illustrious scientist Hermann von Helmholtz. Ellis also mentioned that Helmholtz had used electromagnets to keep a number of tuning forks resonating simultaneously, and that he had been able to create vowel sounds by changing the loudness of the forks. Bell somehow assumed that Helmholtz was actually transmitting the sounds from one telegraphy. In a master stroke of serendipity, Bell had been thrust together with a man almost uniquely suited to become his father-in-law.

Aleck's reputation flourished. In the fall of 1872 he settled in Boston, opening a school for the training of teachers of the deaf. In 1873, he became Professor of Vocal Physiology and Elocution at Boston University, and continued a lively private practice. One of his pupils was George Sanders, a five-year-old boy, born deaf, the son of a prosperous Salem leather merchant. George was to profit greatly from his long tutelage with Bell; and Bell was to profit from the friendship of George's father.

For both Sanders and Hubbard quickly became financial backers of Bell's "hobby"–his electrical researches, when they learned of his extracurricular experiments. Still stimulated by his previous exposure to Helmholtz's work, Bell was resolved to develop what he called a "harmonic telegraph." This instrument would, he hoped, simultaneously transmit tones of different pitches over a single wire, and then unscramble them at the receiving end, using sets of tuning forks. If successful, it would be the basis of a true multiple telegraph – one capable of transmitting many messages at a time over a single line. The multiple (or multiplex) telegraph was the Holy Grail of the Western Union Telegraph Company and of hordes of inventors, including Thomas A. Edison; it was obviously worth a fortune to the man who perfected it. When both Hubbard and Sanders offered to subsidize Bell's work, he agreed, with the proviso that all three share equally in the eventual rewards, if any.

A genius at invention but not a gifted craftsman

Bell was a genius at invention, but he was not a gifted craftsman. Realizing that he lacked the manual skill to assemble the equipment for his various experiments, he went for assistance to the workshop of Charles Williams, on Court Street in Boston, which turned out commercial equipment and fabricated all sorts of electrical apparatus to order. It was a mecca for electrical inventors – Edison had tinkered there some years before. Bell was assigned a bright young man – a mainstay of the shop – to help him. The young man, whose name was Thomas A. Watson, described that first meeting in a 1913 address delivered before the third annual convention of the Telephone Pioneers of America: "In the early winter of 1874 I was making . . . some experimental torpedo exploding apparatus. That apparatus will always be connected in my mind with the telephone, for one day when I was hard at work on it, a tall, slender, quick-motioned man with pale face, black side whiskers, and drooping mustache, big nose and high sloping forehead crowned with bushy, jet black hair, came rushing out of the office and over to my work bench. It was Alexander Graham Bell."

Bell had already conceived, but not tested, the

basic principle of his telephone, probably during the summer of 1874. Now he confided it, early in 1875, to his new friend and disciple. In Watson's words: "One evening when we were resting from our struggles with the [telegraphic] apparatus, Bell said to me, 'Watson, I want to tell you of another idea I have, which I think will surprise you. . . .' I have never forgotten his exact words; they have run in my mind ever since like a mathematical formula. 'If,' he said, 'I could make a current of electricity vary in intensity, precisely as the air varies in density during the production of a sound, I should be able to transmit speech telegraphically.' He then sketched for me an instrument that he thought would do this, and we discussed the possibility of constructing one. I did not make it; it was altogether too costly, and the chances of its working too uncertain to impress his financial backers . . . who were insisting that the wisest thing for Bell to do was to perfect the harmonic telegraph; then he would have money and leisure enough to build air castles like the telephone."

Bell sought encouragement also from Joseph Henry, elder statesman of American science, and director of the Smithsonian Institution in Washington. Bell reviewed his experiments and demonstrated some of his apparatus, learned which of his work was original and which was following on well-trodden paths, and diffidently revealed his plan to transmit speech electrically. Henry proclaimed that it was "the germ of a great invention" and urged Bell to develop it himself, rather than simply publish the concept. When Bell accurately disclaimed the necessary knowledge of electricity, Henry pointedly told him: "Get it!"

Although these words filled Bell with new resolve, they clothed an unconscious irony. Soon after the telephone had made its successful appearance, a leading electrical scientist, Moses G. Farmer, commented to Watson: "That thing has flaunted itself in my very face a dozen times within the last ten years and every time I was too blind to see it. But if Bell had known anything about electricity he would never have invented the telephone." And in later years, Bell himself came to agree.

The moment of discovery

The moment of discovery actually came on the sweltering afternoon of June 2, 1875, in a garret over the Williams electrical workshop. Bell in the receiving room and Watson in the transmitting room were patiently trying to overcome their harmonic telegraph's maddening foibles. The steel organ reeds (substituted for tuning forks) needed constant retuning by means of an adjustment screw. Sometimes, if a reed were screwed down too tightly, it stuck to the pole of the electromagnet beneath it instead of being free to vibrate. When one of Watson's reeds, in the transmitting room, stopped vibrating, Watson plucked at it to free it, and as nothing happened, kept on plucking it. An account of the day published in *Popular Science* describes what happened next: "Suddenly there came a shout from Bell and he rushed in excitedly from the next room, 'What did you do then? Don't change anything. Let me see!'"

Listening to the receiving reed at the other end of the line, Bell heard a completely different sound from the usual transmitter whine–the twang of a plucked reed complete with its timbre, the complex set of tones and overtones that give character to sound. He at once realized that the plucked reed, screwed down too tightly to fulfill its normal, make-or-break, telegraphic function, had instead acted as a diaphragm, and sent continuous, but fluctuating current over the line. In Watson's words: "The circuit had remained unbroken while that strip of magnetized steel by its vibration over the pole of its magnet was generating that marvelous conception of Bell's – a current of electricity that varied in intensity precisely as the air was varying in density within hearing distance of that spring. That undulatory current had passed through the connecting wire to the distant receiver, which, fortunately, was a mechanism that could transform that current back into an extremely faint echo of the sound of the vibrating spring that had generated it, but what was still more fortunate, the right man had that mechanism at his ear. . . . The speaking telephone was born at that moment."

Chance favors the prepared mind

An accident. But, as Pasteur once wrote, "Chance favors the prepared mind." Everything in Bell's background had prepared him for this chance brush with glory. And he instantly seized the opportunity. Contrary to electrical dogma, an induced electric current *could* be strong enough to be useful. And surely he could devise diaphragms better suited to speech than the steel reeds. "All the experimenting that followed that discovery," says Watson, "up to the time the telephone was put into practical use, was largely a matter of working out the details." Within days, the first, crude membrane diaphragm telephone transmitted the faint murmur of Bell's voice to Watson, although the words themselves couldn't be made out. It was not until the following March – March 10, 1876 – that Watson heard "a complete and intelligible sentence." That was, of course, the immortal "Mr. Watson, come here. I want you." In fact, whether Bell actually spilled the now legendary battery acid, and whether, indeed, these were the exact words Bell used, is totally, and immaterially, uncertain. What is clear is that this model of the telelphone, one that used a battery and a variable resistance instead of a magneto transmitter, was the first really successful one. And a powered variable-resistance transmitter made possible the enormous success of the future telephone industry. Three days before, Bell had received his first telephonic patent – possibly the most valuable patent in history.

The news of his discovery was soon broadcast in a way that could not have been better arranged by the most audacious of publicity agents. Again, happy coincidence smoothed the way. That year, 1876, was the year of the great Centennial Exhibition, held in Philadelphia and attended by notables from all over the world. Gardiner Hubbard, Bell's old friend, backer, and soon-to-be father-in-law, was one of three members of the committee on the Massachusetts science and education exhibit. He pressed Bell to participate; the result was that the state's exhibit included a table labeled "Telegraphic and Telephonic Apparatus by A. Graham Bell," which included both the variable-resistance and magnetic versions of the telephone. But Bell resisted going to the exhibition himself; he was immersed in school matters. Mabel, his fiancée, practically had to drag him to the railroad station, because he had, as he wrote his mother the next day, "not the remotest intention of leaving Boston." But, moved at seeing the young girl (she was eighteen) "pale and anxious," Bell got on the train. "What I am going to do in Philadelphia," he wrote, "I cannot tell."

What he did there is history. It is well described in the first of a remarkable series of *Popular Science* articles on the early telephone, written by Fred De Land starting in 1906. (Bell commented that the writer, whom he had never met, "seems to know more about me and what I have done than I know myself.")

At the Centennial Exhibition

Sunday, June 25, 1876, was oppressively hot. It was the day a group of experts including the famous English scientist Sir William Thompson, later Lord Kelvin, was to judge the electrical exhibits. Bell's modest table was tucked in a remote corner of the sweltering exhibition building, by a flight of stairs, and before the moist and exhausted judges reached it they had run out of both time and energy. They probably would simply have not bothered, except that one of them recognized Bell, and insisted on seeing his exhibit. The fact that this person was Pedro II, the portly Emperor of Brazil, was probably of some influence with the other judges. Luckily, again, Dom Pedro had visited Bell at the Boston School for the Deaf just eleven days before, and had formed a warm impression of him. De Land writes: "His Majesty spoke so enthusiastically about the telephone, that, tired as the judges were, they concluded to investigate thoroughly its merits."

First, Sir William listened with the sheet-metal diaphragm of a receiver to his ear as Bell, at the far end of a gallery, sang and spoke into one of his electromagnetic transmitters. The first words Sir William clearly made out were "Do you understand what I say?" Amazed, he ran to tell Bell that he had indeed understood. When Dom Pedro took the receiver, he heard Bell reciting "To be or not to be," leaped from his chair, and shouted, "I hear, I hear," and soon Bell, still spouting Hamlet, saw Dom Pedro galloping toward him at what he called "a very unemperor-like gait."

The telephone had made a stunning impact. One of the experts, Professor George F. Barker of the University of Pennsylvania, wrote: "I was greatly astonished and delighted to hear *for the first time* the transmission of articulate speech electrically. The mode of operation of the instrument was obvious at once, as soon as it was exhibited: it was one of those marvelously simple inventions that causes one to wonder, on seeing it for the first time, that it had not been invented long before."

And Professor T. Sterry Hunt, an eminent Canadian scientist, after dining with Sir William Thompson at the end of that great day, wrote to Bell: "He (Thompson) speaks with much enthusiasm of your achievement. What yesterday he would have declared impossible he has today seen realized, and he declares it the most wonderful thing he has seen in America. You speak of it as an embryo invention, but to him it seems already complete; and he declares that, before long, friends will whisper their secrets over the electric wire."

People will whisper their secrets over the electric wire

Sir William spoke prophetically. More trials followed at the exhibition, and Bell received a Centennial award. The government published reports by Sir William and by Joseph Henry, chairman of the judges. Professor F. A. P. Barnard, president of Columbia University, said he was confident that "the name of the inventor of the telephone would be handed down to posterity with a permanent claim on the gratitude and remembrance of mankind."

In the summer of 1876, Bell successfully transmitted between various points near his parents' home in Brantford, Ontario – the first real long-distance telephony. The distances: four or five miles. Bell and Watson (who gave up his job at the Williams shop and received a one-tenth interest in all Bell's patents) continued experimenting, and conducted more long-distance trials. On February 12, 1877, Bell gave a tremendously popular public demonstration at Lyceum Hall in Salem, where he spoke over an eighteen-mile telephone connection to Watson in their laboratory in Boston. Watson could be heard by those in the hall, shouting, "Hoy! Hoy!"

(This, incidentally, was the form of telephonic address Bell used all his life, resisting "hello" to the end.) Bell happily transmitted to Boston the news story dictated by a reporter for the Boston *Globe*. Next day, the paper published it, under the trumpeting headline: "Sent by Telephone. The First Newspaper Dispatch Sent by a Human Voice Over the Wires." Two young Japanese pupils of Bell proved, beyond any doubt, that the telephone could "talk Japanese."

The first cash Bell obtained directly from his invention was a profit of $149 gained from a demonstration-lecture to a packed house in Salem. With $85 of it, he had a silver miniature of the telephone made for Mabel. Commercial development of the telephone followed very rapidly, and in July 1877, Alexander Graham Bell, with silver and perhaps even golden prospects assured, married Mabel Hubbard. As a wedding gift, he turned over to her about 30 percent of the shares in the newly formed Bell Telephone Company, all that he owned save ten shares, which he kept for sentimental value. It was to prove a gift worthy of a rajah. Thanks to Gardiner Hubbard's business acumen (it was he who insisted on leasing, not selling telephones) and an insatiable demand for the remarkable new device, the Bells went by easy stages from being comfortable, to being well-off, to being rich. By 1881, a mere five years after the laboratory prototype of the telephone first spoke, the Bells were worth about a million dollars, with an income of about $37,000 a year. This came about despite the fact that patent litigation to establish the true authorship of the telephone dragged on for eighteen years. (After 1881, Bell had nothing to do with the development of the telephone business.)

The decision to lease the telephone to subscribers

So there Bell was, just thirty years old, world-famous inventor of the sensation of the day, and with a sizable fortune on the horizon. Another young man might have been quite bowled over. But for Bell, the only real effect seemed to be on his weight. Two months before the wedding, Mabel had written to Alexander's mother, jokingly, "I am beginning to learn that my happiness in life will depend on how well I can feed him." On their nuptial day, the six-foot Bell was a slender 165 pounds. A few months later, Mabel wrote from Scotland, where they were sojourning, "Aleck is perfectly happy with his Edinburgh rolls, Scotch oatmeal porridge and red herring. . . . In fact Aleck is growing tremendously stout, and can hardly get his wedding trousers on now." In the fall, his weight reached 201 pounds, and by Christmas he had outgrown his trousers. Next summer—214 pounds. He never again sank below 200, and ballooned in later life to an imperial 250.

Even when he was close to seventy and suffering from diabetes, he could not resist the lure of forbidden food. When his doctor, summoned to treat an attack of acute indigestion following a wee hours raid on the refrigerator, taxed Bell for the folly of devouring cold potatoes, macaroni and cheese, and Smithfield ham, the inventor replied that it was the best meal he'd enjoyed in an age.

Bell had other idiosyncrasies that tried Mabel's patience for the forty-five years of their remarkably happy married life.

For his wife, by far the worst of these was his nocturnal behavior. Bell was a classic case of the night owl. His natural preference was to retire at about 4:00 A.M., after a night of solitary strolls, and perhaps piano playing, and to sleep through the whole morning. (His breakfast, which he didn't mind eating ice-cold, was simply left on a tray near his bed.) He once wrote Mabel, in expiation of his irritating behavior, "to take night from me is to rob me of life."

Only fellow night owls can properly sympathize with his incredible difficulty in waking up in the morning. His daughter Elsie–born in London, 1878–said that her father was "the soundest sleeper I have ever known. . . . He was so hard to awaken that he often stayed up all night in order to be on time for an early-morning engagement." In 1898, on a tour of Japan, he was summoned to appear before the Emperor at ten in the morning, in full formal dress. Bell looked forward to the whole affair with unmasked loathing. On the fatal morning, his valet managed to oust him from bed, deck him in the hated outfit, and launch him in the appropriate direction. After a brief audience, Bell returned home and tumbled wordlessly into bed. When he woke at 2:00 P.M., he demanded to know when the consul was coming to conduct him to the Emperor.

Bell blamed some of this behavior on sleeplessness caused by very frequent headaches. Many resulted from heat, to which he had a great aversion, and which also caused him annoying rashes. (Bell became an early exponent and practitioner of home air conditioning.) But most of his headaches seemed to be of the "tension" variety, arising when his work was not going well.

Mabel could also never quite reconcile herself to her husband's preference for dark and stormy weather (he shunned the sun) nor to a strain of aloofness, a kind of perpetual questing for solitude. "I often feel like hiding myself away in a corner out of sight," he wrote to Mabel one month after his brilliant success at the Philadelphia Centennial Exhibition. Even though he came to be the cheerful and staunch patriarch of a large clan, his son-in-law

David Fairchild could say of him with justice, after Bell died: "Mr. Bell led a peculiarly isolated life; I have never known anyone who spent so much of his time alone." Perhaps this aloofness, the solitary walks at night, the weekend flights to an isolated houseboat at his summer estate in Nova Scotia, his endless piano playing in an otherwise silent house – perhaps this was characteristic of the inventor's mind. And perhaps Bell himself summed it up best when he wrote ". . . I somehow or other appear to be more interested in *things* than people. . . ."

The quest for solitude

Bell did indulge one bizarre but harmless eccentricity. This lover of trees and mountains, lakes and rocks, rain and wind could not suffer moonlight to fall on him, or any of his loved ones, while he slept. So on nights of the full moon, before going to bed, he tiptoed round the sleeping house, drawing curtains and arranging screens to shield his family from its baleful rays.

None of this character analysis, of course, explains why Bell, his fame and fortune assured at age thirty, did not simply enjoy life as a lionized genius and take it easy. For forty-five years he never stopped working hard at his twin careers of inventing and teaching the deaf. One key was certainly his enormous curiosity, his constant wondering! (In 1879, he bought a copy of the Encyclopaedia Britannica with the intention of reading it from beginning to end.) Another was probably his fear that the invention of the telephone was to be the pinnacle of his career, making the rest of his life a long anticlimax.

In this fear, Bell was justified. But what an anticlimax!

Until his death at age seventy-five, Bell's restless spirit ranged over a dazzling array of subjects, from magazine publishing and progressive education to aviation and eugenics. He never stopped inventing. But none of the things he developed in those forty-five years every came close to being another telephone. At least, not in posterity's opinion.

* * *

At two of a hushed and luminous morning, on August 2, 1922, as Mabel called his name, he raised his lids and smiled. She implored him not to leave her. His fingers spoke into her hand a sign for "no." Then he died.

There is no monument, simply a marker and the word of his calling – inventor

Bell was buried where he wished to be at the top of his mountain on August 4, at 6:25 P.M. All telephone service throughout the United States was suspended then, for one minute. There is no monument, simply a marker, set into a rock, with Bell's name, the dates of his birth and death, his calling – *inventor* – and the words he had specifically requested: "Died a Citizen of the United States."

He might have included in his epitaph some words from an interview he gave in 1902, about the life of an inventor: "It is pretty hard and steady work. But then, it is my pleasure, too."

Innovation & Achievement

1879

Thomas A. Edison.

7

The lamp continued to burn. . . .
None of us could go to bed.
We sat and just watched it
with anxiety growing into elation.
It lasted about forty-five hours.

"In 1878, I went down to see Professor Barker, at Philadelphia, and he showed me an arc lamp–the first I had seen. Then a little later I saw another–I think it was one of Brush's make–and the whole outfit, engine, dynamo, and one or two lamps, was traveling around the country with a circus. At that time Wallace and Moses G. Farmer had succeeded in getting ten or fifteen lamps to burn together in a series, which was considered a very wonderful thing. It happened that at the time I was more or less at leisure, because I had just finished working on the carbon-button telephone, and this electric light idea took possession of me. It was easy to see what the thing needed: it wanted to be subdivided. The light was too bright and too big. What we wished for was little lights, and a distribution of them to people's houses in a manner similar to gas. Grovernor P. Lowry thought that perhaps I could succeed in solving the problem, and he raised a little money and formed the Edison Electric Light Company. The way we worked was that I got a sum of money a week and employed a certain number of men, and we went ahead to see what we could do.

An extraordinary feat of creativity

"We soon saw that the subdivision never could be accomplished unless each light was independent of every other. Now it was plain enough that they could not burn in series. Hence they must burn in multiple arc. It was with this conviction that I started. I was fired with the idea of the incandescent lamp as opposed to the arc lamp, so I went to work and got some very fine platinum wire drawn. Experiment with this, however, resulted in failure, and then we tried mixing in with the platinum about 10 percent of iridium, but we could not force that high enough without melting it. After that came a lot of experimenting—covering the wire with oxide of cerium and a number of other things.

"Then I got a great idea. I took a cylinder of zirconia and wound about a hundred feet of the fine platinum wire on it coated with magnesia from the syrupy acetate. What I was after was getting a high-resistance lamp, and I made one that way that worked up to 40 ohms. But the oxide developed the phenomena now familiar to electricians, and the lamp short-circuited itself. After that we went fishing around and trying all sorts of shapes and things to make a filament that would stand. We tried silicon and boron, and a lot of things that I have forgotten now. The funny part of it was that I never thought in those days that a carbon filament would answer, because a fine hair of carbon was so sensitive to oxidation. Finally, I thought I would try it because we had got very high vacua and good conditions for it.

"Well, we sent out and bought some cotton thread, carbonized it, and made the first filament. We had already managed to get pretty high vacua, and we thought, maybe, the filament would be stable. We built the lamp and turned on the current. It lit up, and in the first few breathless minutes we measured its resistance quickly and found it was 275 ohms – all we wanted. Then we sat down and looked at that lamp. We wanted to see how long it would burn. The problem was solved – if the filament would last. The day was – let me see – October 21, 1879. We sat and looked, and the lamp continued to burn, and the longer it burned the more fascinated we were. None of us could go to bed, and there was no sleep for any of us for forty hours. We sat and just watched it with anxiety growing into elation. It lasted about forty-five hours, and then I said, 'If it will burn that number of hours now, I know I can make it burn a hundred.' We saw that carbon was what we wanted, and the next question was what kind of carbon. I began to try various things, and finally I carbonized a strip of bamboo from a Japanese fan, and saw that I was on the right track. But we had a rare hunt finding the real thing. I sent a schoolmaster to Sumatra and another fellow up the Amazon, while William H. Moore, one of my associates, went to Japan and got what we wanted there. We made a contract with a supplier to provide the proper fiber and cultivate and cross fertilize bamboo until he got exactly the quality we required. One man went down to Havana, and the day he got there he was seized with yellow fever and died in the afternoon. When I read the cable message to the boys, about a dozen of them jumped up and asked for his job. Those fellows were a bright lot of chaps, and sometimes it was hard to select the right ones."

One of the greatest inventions in history

That is the whole history of the invention of the incandescent light according to Edison's modest statement in an old number of the *Electrical Review*. His thirteen months of unwearied experimenting with different metals in his search for a suitable filament – carbon points he had hardly considered for a moment – were forgotten, but some account of those days of anxiety, dejection, hope, and final triumph bear mention lest the reader come to the erroneous conclusion that the invention of incandescent electric lighting was the thing of ease Edison would have us suppose. Had any other man encountered the difficulties – or half of them – that Edison did, we might still be reading by gas and studying by candlelight.

* * *

When Edison was wrestling with a major problem like his incandescent lamp, his day at the laboratory knew no quitting time and he worked on, far into the night. A few steps would have taken him home to bed – but, when weariness overcame him, he preferred to curl up on a bench for a brief nap and then be at it again. It was a tribute to the fanatical devotion he inspired in his closest aides, who had the satisfaction of taking part in creating his wonders, that they were willing to follow his example.

An unorthodox fixture of his laboratory was a pipe organ – on which Edison was "more than a fair performer," his assistant Francis Jehl wrote in *Popular Science*. After a midnight snack brought in by his night watchman, he and his men were wont to join in a rousing songfest, with Edison at the organ. Sometimes his expert glass blower, Ludwig Boehm, entertained them with German songs on his zither.

A public demonstration

Edison invited the public to a demonstration of his incandescent lamp on New Year's Eve, 1879. The Pennsylvania Railroad ran special trains to Menlo Park. Some 3,000 people came to see the Wizard's latest marvel – and it was a show to remember.

White snow on the ground reflected the radiance of the new electric bulbs in lampposts, all along the half-mile way from the station up the road to Edison's laboratory, which was ablaze with electric light.

So were Edison's home, and Sarah Jordan's boarding house near his lab, the home of many of his aides. They were the first residences ever lit by electric light. In all, more than 400 bulbs were wired up, and fed with current from a big generator in a special building near the lab.

Edison himself showed the milling visitors around, and encouraged them to lay loose bulbs, with conducting rods attached, across feeder mains in his laboratory and watch them magically light up. After the big show, his men found eight bulbs gone – some of the visitors had been irresistibly tempted to pocket them as souvenirs of the historic occasion.

Away from Menlo Park, at that time, incandescent electric bulbs would be useless, for lack of electric wiring to plug them into. The next goal Edison set himself was to build a great central lighting plant for New York City, with electric mains leading to wiring installed in the buildings of customers. Since such a system was unprecedented, Edison had to design everything for it from scratch – the generators, the underground mains, the lamp sockets (which by now held bulbs with filaments made from bamboo fibers, as they would be for ten years), and such practical details as electric meters to gauge a customer's bills for the electricity he used. The monumental task was completed by September 4, 1882, when Edison's pioneer central station on Pearl Street in New York City went into service.

The incandescent lamp was by no means the full story of Edison's accomplishments during the "Menlo Park period" that marked the peak of his career. It would take a book to detail all his inventions and patents during those eventful years.

A picturesque feature of the final ones was America's first electric railroad, which grew to a three-mile experimental line. Using one of his "long-waisted

Mary Ann" dynamos as a motor, Edison built a forty-mile-an-hour passenger locomotive that pulled a trainload of ninety people—and a slower freight locomotive for heavier duty. One rail of the track conducted electric power to the locomotive, and the other rail formed the return circuit.

Forward-looking vision

The trials were enlivened by an accident when Kruesi, who was driving, overenthusiastically rounded a curve at full forty-mile-an-hour speed and the locomotive jumped the track—catapulting him face down beside the roadbed, and another man somersaulting into underbrush. Fortunately no one was hurt, a *Popular Science* account said, and the engine was set back on the tracks as good as ever. But it proved too early to interest the Northern Pacific or other U.S. railroads in electrifying their systems, and Edison's forward-looking vision of electric railways led nowhere at the time.

Married life had set well with Edison. The untimely death of his wife Mary in 1884, from typhoid fever, left a great void in his scheme of things. Sympathetic friends saw to it that he met likely successors, and the matchmakers scored when he was introduced to charming, cultured Mina Miller. Although only twenty, and eighteen years Edison's junior, she was wise beyond her years in the ways of inventors—being the daughter of a successful and wealthy Ohio one herself.

Edison taught her the telegrapher's Morse code, which could be transmitted just as well by a squeeze of the fingers as by a telegraph key—and they found a new use for the versatile means of communication. Holding hands, they could exchange sweet nothings in complete privacy. One day Edison summoned up the courage to ask her, in Morse, if she would marry him. Her answer was two pairs of dots for *Y*, a single dot for *E*, and three dots for *S*.

They were married in February of 1886, when Edison was thirty-nine. In time they would have three children; and one of these, Charles, would become a future governor of New Jersey.

To Edison it was time for a complete change of scene. He bought a palatial new home, called Glenmont, in the Llewellyn Park neighborhood of West Orange, New Jersey. Within a year, he moved his laboratory from Menlo Park to its final site in West Orange, where its newly built three-story brick building would soon be the nucleus of a cluster of structures housing Edison enterprises.

The story of Edison's ventures at West Orange from 1887 to 1910 almost defies being told in chronological sequence, because major events in so many of his endeavors stretched out into overlapping periods. Even at the expense of jumping about in dates, it seems better to stick to one of his principal projects at a time.

One of the pioneers of motion pictures, Edison became a movie mogul. On the same day, July 31, 1891, he successfully applied for patents on a movie camera, which he called the Kinetographic Camera, and a viewer of the peephole type named the Kinetoscope. Having provided the equipment, Edison began producing movies himself.

Willing to try, not afraid to fail

At his West Orange laboratory, he built the world's first motion-picture studio. The wooden building admitted direct sunlight to its stage through a wide door in the roof, and turned on a pivot to follow the sun. A tar paper covering and a black-painted interior, to eliminate reflections, gave it the nickname of the "Black Maria."

At first the studio produced short films – only a minute or so in length. Subjects included a dancer named Carmencita, performing bears, fencing matches, and feats of horsemanship, a *Popular*

Science writer recalled. A few of the day's celebrities received the top fee of fifty dollars for appearing before the camera. (Among these was "Gentleman Jim" Corbett of contemporary boxing fame.)

Parlors lined with batteries of coin-operated peepshow-type viewers opened in cities, and attracted crowds to see the brief films.

For larger audiences, promoters urged Edison to develop a projector that could throw movies on a theater screen. Cool to the suggestion, he almost missed a great opportunity. In 1895 another inventor, Thomas Armat, came up with a theater-screen movie projector. Before anyone else could snap it up, an intermediary persuaded Edison and Armat to make a deal. Edison acquired the projector – and it was agreeable to both parties for him to make and market it under his famous name, rather than Armat's little-known one.

What resulted was the storied "nickelodeon," the five-cent theater. The Sears, Roebuck catalog of 1902 offered prospective operators the "Edison Projection Kinetoscope" (with either an electric arc lamp or a calcium burner) for $105; and a wide selection of films, some twenty minutes in length, "exclusively made in the Edison laboratory." Such was the popularity of the innovation that the 1908 Sears, Roebuck catalog declared, "The five-cent theater is here to stay. It fills a want that has existed in every community for a clean, up to date amusement . . . almost any vacant storeroom can be made into a five-cent theater by removing the glass front and replacing it with a regular theater front," complete with ticket booth, of which it printed an illustration. A hit with audiences was a prototype of film dramas, *The Great Train Robbery,* released by Edison in 1904.

From the first, Edison experimented with synchronizing phonograph recordings with his pictures, anticipating the talkies; but they had to wait until much later to catch on with the public.

Patents controlled by Edison ruled the country's movie industry up to as late as 1917.

New ventures

Edison the Iron Miner should have had a place in history alongside Edison the Moviemaker. His iron-mining venture of 1890-1900 was remarkable for the brilliantly original engineering that went into it–though today it is almost forgotten, because an unpredictable quirk of fortune cheated it of well-deserved success.

A prized ore of iron was black magnetite–popularly called lodestone–which attracts a compass needle and, conversely, is attracted by a magnet. Back in 1880 at Menlo Park, Edison had invented a magnetic separator that could extract this iron-bearing ore from powdered rock containing it. In 1889 he sent a crew with special magnetic needles on a survey from Canada to North Carolina, to look for the magnetic ore at 1,000-foot intervals and report what they found. They discovered a surprising number of promising deposits–most notably, a veritable mountain of magnetite ore overlooking Ogdensburg in the picturesque Sparta Mountains of northwestern New Jersey's Sussex County.

Tempered by the competitive realities

In 1890 Edison began construction there of a huge iron-mining and ore-concentrating plant, which became the center of a mountaintop community called Edison, New Jersey. The key to success, he figured, would be an economical way to recover the estimated 200 million tons of magnetite from three times as much barren rock with which it was intermingled.

Boldly Edison proposed to tear down the whole mountain of ore and reduce it to powder for his magnetic separator. Dynamite was an expensive source of energy, he reasoned, compared to steam power from coal. So he would use blasting only to knock loose great boulders of ore from the face of his open-pit workings. Out the window went the conventional next step of drilling and blasting each boulder into pieces small enough for an ordinary rock crusher to handle.

Instead, five-ton boulders were picked up bodily by the largest steam shovel yet built, and loaded into skips aboard narrow-gauge rail cars, to be hauled right to his mill. There, a traveling crane seized the loaded skips, and dumped the boulders into the most awesome mechanical rock-breaker the world had ever seen.

With a rending crash that could be heard from afar, a boulder as big as a piano was literally torn to pieces between a pair of six-foot-diameter "giant rolls" with projecting spikes, spun up to a surface speed of nearly a mile a minute by belts from a 700-horsepower steam engine. At the moment of impact, the belts could slip on the drive pulleys – an Edison innovation that averted damage to the driving machinery from the shock. The sheer momentum of the heavy, speeding rolls sufficed to crack the boulder into pieces that would drop between them. Then the drive belts took hold again and brought the rolls back up to full speed for the next boulder.

Successively smaller rolls took turns in reducing the rock fragments' size – and ultimately they became a flourlike powder. It sifted in a thin stream past powerful magnets, which deflected the falling grains of magnetite into a bin to one side, while the barren rock dropped straight down into another.

The mill's final product was "briquettes" of the concentrated iron ore, made by mixing the black powder with a resinous binder and pressing it into round cakes, three inches in diameter and half as thick. The binder kept the briquettes from crumbling and made them weatherproof, so they could be shipped to market in open railway cars. They looked like plump, burnt-black hamburger patties—but if you picked one up, its telltale weight bespoke its heavy content of iron.

By 1897 the mill was ready for trial-scale production. Like a theatrical producer awaiting the critics' reviews of a play, Edison hung upon reports from the first users of the briquettes. They were enthusiastic. A typical report of a blast furnace trial by the Crane Iron Works at Catasauqua, Pennsylvania, showed the briquettes served better than standard iron ores—raising the furnace's output and reducing its fuel consumption at the same time.

As the word spread, orders rolled in. In 1898 and 1899, the mill was running at capacity. Then came the catastrophic blow.

Not always a smooth course

Iron ore in fabulous quantities, easily mined, was discovered in the Mesabi Range of Minnesota, along the coast of Lake Superior. The new Sault Sainte Marie Canal gave it ready access to market—and the price of high-grade iron ore tumbled from $6.50 to $3.50 a ton.

At his mining headquarters in 1900, Edison studied his engineers' gloomy reports on the Mesabi development. Then he made the only possible decision: "Blow the whistle and pay the men off. We can't compete with this."

With abandonment of his iron works, two million dollars—largely Edison's own money—went down the great hole he had dug. A game loser, he remarked to a close associate, "Well, it's all gone, but we had a hell of a good time spending it."

He paid back every cent contributed by other backers. Then he plunged into new enterprises to recoup his own losses.

For the unique rock-breaking machinery he had devised, he found another use – and went into the business of making Portland cement. Edison cement plants of his own design introduced monster rotating kilns 150 feet long, compared to standard sixty-foot size. Contrary to skeptics' expectations, the plants were successful, and Edison became one of the country's largest producers of cement. His product went into New York City's Yankee Stadium, as well as a part of the Panama Canal, and countless buildings and bridges.

A well of creativity that never ran dry

A pet idea he proposed in 1909, *Popular Science* noted, was to construct "instant houses" by pouring a free-flowing concrete mix he had developed into iron molds. He believed the houses could be erected in six hours, and ready to move into in three days. Actual poured-concrete houses demonstrated his idea a decade later.

In 1900 Edison embarked upon another major ten-year project – to develop a radical new kind of storage battery, which he thought would replace the standard lead-acid kind, and power electric automobiles of the future.

The result was his nickel-iron-alkaline battery – and the course of perfecting it was a struggle against "bugs" that plagued the first ones to be marketed. In the end the new storage battery was a success – though on a much more limited scale than Edison had optimistically pictured when he began.

What time showed the battery could and couldn't do was assessed by a *Popular Science* article about it in 1959:

"Edison had hoped, above all, that it would be adaptable for automotive traction. Automobile traction proved to be just what it was *not* suited for. Nor was it useful as a starter battery. Its voltage capacity tended to be lower than that of contemporary lead batteries, so that one needed more Edison cells for a given task – which offset their advantage of lighter weight.

"On the other hand, the beautifully constructed Edison battery was found particularly useful where dependability and long life were important, as for standby purposes at power plants, and for railway signaling; or to provide current for miners' lamps, train lights, and other railway and marine appliances. A remarkably wide field of usage was developed in industries such as mining and quarrying (for firing blasts), on merchant vessels, and on ships of war."

Personal characteristics

Contemporary accounts tell us what Edison looked like as a man. He was of chunky build, five foot ten in height and with a weight of about 185 pounds, which varied little for years. Gray eyes peered searchingly from beneath a high-domed forehead – in later years, "thatched as Pike's Peak in winter." Bluff and hearty in manner, he conversed informally in language well-laced with slang, with an oddly high-pitched voice that could become nasal at times.

His laboratory garb, original with him, bordered on the ridiculous. Instead of wearing a chemical worker's rubberized apron to protect his clothes from acids and such, Edison flapped about, one reporter noted, in "a long frock of checked gingham, which buttons close at the chin and reaches to his heels . . . a sight to laugh at, until you remember that it is Edison."

No teetotaler, Edison enjoyed a bottle of beer or a glass of champagne now and then. He smoked ten to twenty cigars daily – and kept a package of chewing tobacco in his pocket, too.

Rough-hewn Edison was a notorious practical joker. Neither his laboratory workers nor his social guests were spared. For a prize example, the tale is told that when he once invited friends to a steak dinner, he cut up slabs of half-inch-thick leather belting with his jackknife and had his cook heat them in an oven, cover them with gravy, and serve them to the unsuspecting diners. When he was sufficiently convulsed by watching their futile attempts to eat the mock "steaks," these were whisked away and the real ones brought in. The prelude could hardly have been much of an appetizer.

But as the years mellowed the boy in him, another brand of Edison humor appeared in his dry wit. Did he think, a *Popular Science* interviewer asked him, that mankind had progressed mentally in recent decades or millennia? He replied he definitely believed the proportion of honest, humane, and highly intelligent men was increasing; but, he added with a twinkle, "The Lord appears to be in no hurry."

Besides new projects, Edison worked at West Orange on unfinished business left over from his Menlo Park days.

Unfinished business

His lamp filaments had been made for the past ten years from bamboo, the best material tried at Menlo Park, but he was still looking for a better one. He found it in "squirted cellulose," a synthetic product he made by forcing a cellulose material through a die. This gave a filament of perfectly uniform thickness, avoiding hot spots that would shorten its life when it was lit.

Edison returned to his long-neglected phonograph. His work on it had been pushed aside by his preoccupation with electric light. Now its improvement became urgent to meet the competition of rival phonographs like the Graphophone, introduced in 1887 by Alexander Graham Bell and associates, which used cylinder records of wax-coated cardboard. Edison countered with an all-wax cylinder record, and by intensive effort developed a new phonograph to play it.

Disc records, pioneered by Emile Berliner and adopted by leading companies like Victor and Columbia, came into vogue in the early 1900s. Edison held out until 1910, when he and his "insomnia squad" worked day and night for weeks, without leaving his laboratory, to perfect his "diamond-disc" records and a phonograph to go with them.

Edison had ideas all his own of what a disc record should be. His discs, nearly a quarter inch thick and weighing almost a pound apiece, looked like millstones compared to other makers' wafer-thin ones – and would fill a shelf or record cabinet in short order. Until the late 1920s they were "hill-and-dale" recordings, rather than the "lateral" ones that dominated the market long before then. Edison's own studio recorded the many famed artists they featured.

A striking phonograph innovation was a forty-minute Edison disc record, described and illustrated in *Popular Science* in early 1927. The invention of the modern long-play record in 1948 is credited to Peter Goldmark, but Edison must be rated as a pioneer.

Legends and myths

Legends and myths grow up around famous men, and Edison was no exception. His mail, his confidential secretary William H. Meadowcroft recalled, long included inquiries about the "Edison star" that the inventor was supposed to launch daily in the evening sky. Actually it was just a yarn, concocted by a reporter at the time of the incandescent lamp's debut, and not intended to be taken seriously.

Once an interviewer reported Edison was working on a loudspeaker for receiving spirit messages. Edison long evaded other reporters' questions about it, but finally confessed sponsoring the myth himself, and a *Popular Science* writer told how the tale was born.

"That man," Edison said of the interviewer, "came to see me on one of the coldest days of the year. His nose was blue and his teeth were chattering. I really had nothing to tell him, but I hated to disappoint him—so I made up the story about communicating with the spirits. . . It was all a joke." Not knowing it, the reporter happily bore away a "scoop" of a sort.

With the outbreak of World War I, Edison relieved U.S. shortages of imported chemicals by designing a factory that produced a ton a day of synthetic carbolic acid, and plants making coal-tar derivatives that are said to have led the way in development of the American coal-tar chemical industry.

In 1915 the Secretary of the Navy asked Edison to head a board to devise new military weapons for national defense. It was a task abhorrent to him, for he hated war; but he considered it his patriotic duty to accept, and contributed many original ideas of his own. Perhaps to his relief, the conservative Navy brass never got around to adopting any of them.

In 1916, Edison at sixty-nine was introduced to the pleasures of camping out, close to nature, by his good friends Henry Ford, Harvey Firestone, and the naturalist John Burroughs. Thereafter they took an annual camping vacation together, traveling by car to peaceful spots remote from the workaday world for an outing of ten days or so. When Burroughs died in 1921, President Harding accepted their invitation to take his place. They were dude campers, taking along a chef, and tents lit by Edison's storage batteries. Edison brought books to read, often dozed, and joined the others in swapping yarns late into the night.

In 1927, at Edison's age of eighty, his great lifework was nearly done—though he would have refused to admit it. That year he began his last major project, a four-year search for a domestic rubber-yielding plant that could make the nation independent of foreign rubber.

His long robust health was finally failing. His loyal associates knew it, and made allowances for his uncharacteristic testiness in the laboratory. Knowing he would go on working regardless, his wife encouraged him to undertake the rubber project, primarily because it would spare him the rigors of northern winters. The work of growing and testing semitropical plants could best be done at an experimental plantation in Fort Myers, Florida, where he had earlier acquired a winter home that could be his headquarters.

His last major project

In all, Edison tested more than 17,000 different plants – and found as many as forty domestic species that would yield appreciable quantities of rubber. One promising candidate was desert milkweed, a leafless shrub, reported a *Popular Science* interviewer, Frank Parker Stockbridge, in December 1927. But, surprisingly, the best turned out to be goldenrod, which could be grown anywhere in the country and harvested by machinery. Toward that end, Edison bred a strain of goldenrod more than ten feet tall.

For once, though, Edison's trial-and-error technique was unequal to an impossible task. Not even the most promising plants that he tested proved able to yield rubber at a cost competitive with the imported kind. The net result of the whole project was a set of goldenrod-rubber tires that his friend Harvey Firestone had custom-made for Edison's Ford car. By the time of World War II, the answer that Edison had vainly sought in nature was found in synthetic rubber made from chemicals.

The highlights of Edison's final years were honors

he had so richly earned by his past achievements.

In 1927 the prestigious National Academy of Sciences elected him to membership. It was a fitting put-down for some of his learned critics of the past, who had looked down their noses at his comparative lack of formal academic qualifications for the ambitious projects he undertook.

The Golden Jubilee of Light

A Congressional medal awarded to Edison in 1928 was a curtain raiser for the following year's national celebration of the fiftieth anniversary of his incandescent lamp – the "golden jubilee of light."

The scene of the golden jubilee's climax, attended by President Hoover, was a unique tribute to Edison – a reconstruction of Edison's Menlo Park laboratory, at Dearborn, Michigan, by his friend Henry Ford.

Ford had spared no expense or effort to reproduce it meticulously in every detail. Having bought the Menlo Park site, Ford scoured it for all the remains that could still be found. The abandoned building – successively used as a church, a dance hall, and a chicken shed – had finally been torn to pieces by nearby farmers for lumber to mend homes and barns. Ford bought every scrap of the authentic lumber he could find around the countryside.

Like an archaeologist, Ford recovered and restored relics buried in the ground – among them, Edison's broken laboratory mortar and pestle. Ford tracked down, and bought up, genuine pieces of Edison's Menlo Park equipment that had become scattered all over the country.

To put it all together, just as it once had been, Ford needed expert help – and found it when he located the only survivor of Edison's Menlo Park team, Francis Jehl, in Europe and brought him to America for the task.

Carloads of Menlo Park soil, brought to Dearborn

and spread on the ground around the rebuilt laboratory of half a century before, were the finishing touch.

When Edison and his wife arrived in Dearborn two days ahead of the great October 21 celebration, Ford gave him a preview of the big surprise for him. As Edison approached the faithfully reconstructed laboratory, he could hardly believe his eyes. The surprise was capped when the door opened and he was greeted with open arms by Francis Jehl, whom he hadn't seen for forty years. With tears in his eyes, Edison embraced his old assistant.

What Edison saw inside completed his sensation of being transported backward in time to fifty years before. There were his Sprengel vacuum pump, his potbellied stove, the pipe organ at the back wall, and all his Menlo Park laboratory furnishings arranged exactly as they once had been. Library shelves were stocked with precisely the same books, including bound volumes of *Popular Science,* that Edison had kept at hand.

Almost overcome with emotion, the frail old man passed it off with a quip. "Well," he told Ford, "you've got this just about ninety-nine and one-half percent perfect." When Ford anxiously inquired what was wrong with the other half percent, Edison laughingly replied, "We never kept it as clean as this!"

Two days later the climactic event of the golden jubilee took place when, in the presence of the President and other onlookers, Edison and Jehl reenacted the making of the first successful incandescent lamp—and a radio announcer's description of the ceremony ended triumphantly with, "It lights!"

A banquet followed and Edison was escorted to his place of honor at the head table. Exhausted by the gala program and the emotional impact of his

Dearborn visit, he was unable to eat and his deafness kept him from hearing a word of the speeches of praise by the President and other notables. At last all eyes turned to him. Unsteadily he arose, managed a few graceful words of acknowledgment – and then, his duty done, collapsed into his chair.

He was a sicker man than anyone had known. A medical examination found him suffering from what proved to be a hopeless combination of gastric ulcers, diabetes, and Bright's disease. Back home in West Orange, his visits to his laboratory dwindled and ended.

Tenderly Mina Edison nursed him as he waited for what could only be the end. His last words were, "It is very beautiful over there," and then he lapsed into a coma. Early the next morning, on October 18, 1931, he peacefully stopped breathing. At the age of eighty-four, the human dynamo had run down.

An astounding total of 1,093 patents

Posthumously Edison was granted the last four of his astounding total of 1,093 patents.

In retrospect, Edison's fantastic total of inventions was extraordinary for their quality as well as their quantity.

There were rare exceptions; anyone of his stature was entitled to indulge a strange whimsy now and then, and a *Popular Science* article, "Flops of Famous Inventors," recalled a dilly: Edison actually patented a "Vocal Engine," to be powered by speaking into a telephone mouthpiece! (Forty brass bands playing at once, the article opined, could barely yield power enough to light an ordinary lamp bulb.) Ironically Edison tossed off both this brainstorm and an anachronistic scheme for non-electric "telephoning" over a building's gas pipes at just about the time his carbon-button transmitter made a revolutionary improvement in Bell's telephone.

Not even in Edison's round-the-clock life was

there time enough for any one man to carry all his great inventions to final perfection. That may help to explain his readiness to stick stubbornly, in many cases, to the original version that worked.

His first successful carbon-button telephone transmitter, as is known, was of lampblack from a kerosene-lamp chimney–and so the raw material for his succeeding ones came from an inelegant "lampblack factory" consisting of row upon row of smoking kerosene lamps. Only later did telephone makers switch to carbon granules from "telephone coal," a high grade of anthracite.

The first phonographs Edison marketed, like his original one, played primitive tinfoil records. How he was forced by competition to go to wax-cylinder records and finally to disc records (of his unconventional thick design) has been told. Only in the late 1920s did thin Edison discs like everyone else's appear, just before radio's competition and the period's Great Depression wiped out the Edison record business.

In the fashion of his time, Edison favored direct current, and used it in his electric-lighting plants. He took a dim view of alternating-current systems developed not long afterward by the Tesla-Westinghouse team. By hindsight that was a mistake. Because New York City pioneered in adopting Edison's electric lighting, dwellers in some areas of the city were still stuck with direct current, and unable to use the alternating-current appliances that ultimately prevailed, as late as in the middle of the twentieth century.

Edison's movie camera and his peepshow-type viewer seemed to him a complete motion-picture system. Until he was reluctantly persuaded to acquire another inventor's movie-screen projector, his vision seems to have had a blind spot for the infinitely greater possibilities of movies for theater audiences. Recovery of his fumble gave him a rich new source of income, especially welcome after his staggering financial loss in his ill-starred iron-mining enterprise.

All in all, it took generations to finish everything Edison had started. But the credit rightfully goes to him for starting it.

* * *

The ultimate meaning of invention

The opportunity to try out ideas, uninhibited by concerns about manpower or materials and with complete reliance in the skills and talents of the craftsmen around him, gave Edison a capability possessed by no inventor in history before him. This expansive approach should not be confused with the old image of the ill-directed ransacking of nature's storehouse for lamp filament material or other pejorative parts of the legend of Edison the empirical experimenter. There were indeed areas of research in which Edison had to work blindly, but this was hardly a special characteristic of his work nor unexpected in any ambitious technical enterprise. Edison's resources, however, allowed him to explore blind alleys as well as to exploit inspirations with an efficiency and speed that demonstrated for all the real virtues of Menlo Park.

The capital that could be mustered by his reputation was indispensable also in the fulfillment of the Edison promise at Pearl Street. To be sure, the caution and conservatism of Wall Street asserted themselves sufficiently to force Edison to put much of his own money into various manufacturing enterprises for the Edison system. But this detracted little from his ability to summon resources in amounts rarely placed in an inventor's hands. If, in hindsight, Edison's vision seemed wonderfully complete, it was due as much to this command over the means to make the vision whole as to an approach particularly suited to the creation of systems. Indeed, for most of Edison's career, achievements of technical insight are difficult to distinguish from achievements owing more to the great resourses he was able to bring to bear on the problems at hand. His "invention factories" were so successful in both concept and execution that the personal element in the inventive act became less distinct as time went on. For this reason, the claim that Edison's greatest invention was the routinization of invention itself has much merit, even if it does not follow that he set the pattern for the corporate research and development laboratories of the twentieth century.

However, invention is not routine. Certainly, great inventions are not, and the incandescent electric light was one of the greatest in history. This is true, in part for the enormous impact it had on our modern technological culture, because it was, as has been pointed out, the indisputable starting point for the creation of the electric power systems that move, control, and inform our life and work. But the greatness of the electric light as an invention does not rest on that alone. The electric light – the lamp and all the power, distribution, and control technology that went with it – was the product of an extraordinary feat of creativity. It is in this creativity that we must seek to understand the ultimate meaning of invention. Other realms in our culture, such as art, music, literature, and science (to name only the most obvious), are commonly scrutinized for evidence about the process of creation. The study of a painting, a symphony, a poem, or a theory in great detail and with careful attention to the psychological, social, and cultural conditions surrounding its emergence is a common and accepted activity. Such study, it is thought, will bring us closer to the creator and the achievement, will foster our understanding of the values of human culture, and will, just possibly, allow each of us to enhance the expressions of creativity in our own lives.

Innovation & Achievement

1903

Orville Wright
Wilbur Wright

8

We pushed back the doors
and looked outside over the dunes.
It was clearly hopeless
to wait for the wind to soften.
The time had come.

Steady winds from the northeast and long swells of the Atlantic Ocean roll incessantly onto the sand bars and beaches of the Carolina coast. The beaches are windstripped, desolate, and lonely. A sand bar separates Albemarle, Pamlico, and Roanoke Sounds from the ocean, and one stretch of it has a name – Kitty Hawk.

On the cold, bleak morning of December 17, 1903, two men pushed back the doors of a temporary shelter to look out at the weather. They were brothers, named Orville and Wilbur Wright. They were lean, thin-faced men, wearing conventional business suits and high starched white collars. Orville, thirty-two, was a shade over five feet ten, about an inch and a half taller than his thirty-six-year-old brother Wilbur. Orville had a mustache, and sometimes he liked to tease. Wilbur had a poker-faced, wry Ohio sense of humor. Orville, being the younger brother, every so often reminded Wilbur to say "we" when he said "I."

The surf pounded, ice floes moved down Albemarle Sound, and the white beach sand flew on the twenty-seven-mile-an-hour wind.

At ten o'clock in the morning it was clearly useless to wait any longer in the hope that the wind might soften. The two brothers sent up a flag to the top of a mast as a gathering signal to the men at the small U. S. Life-Saving Station south of the camp on the hundred-foot sand dune called Kill Devil Hill. While waiting for the men to come, the brothers dragged out their "flying machine"–a biplane with white muslin wings, about forty feet across. The stretched rectangles of cloth were called "aeroplanes." Earlier, on March 23 of that same year, the Wrights had written to the U. S. Patent Office: "Our invention relates to that class of flying machines in which the weight is sustained by the reactions resulting when one or more aeroplanes are moved through the air edgewise at a small angle of incidence."

The flying machine was intended to take off from a little two-wheel truck, made from bicycle wheel hubs, that fitted a rail made of two-by-fours.

The Wrights, leaning against the wind, were laying track when the five men arrived from the station to help and, by witnessing one of the most historic events of all time, to achieve footnote immortality: J. T. Daniels, W. S. Dough, A. D. Etheridge, W. C. Brinkly, and a boy from Nag's Head, Johnny Moore.

The biting cold made work difficult

"The biting cold made work difficult," wrote Orville Wright in his diary that day. "We had to warm up frequently in our living room, where we had a fire in an improvised stove made of a carbide can."

About twenty-five minutes after ten, the engine was started, and the propellers turned slowly during warm-up. At exactly 10:35 A.M., Orville, squinting against the wind, climbed through the wire struts of the machine and lay face downward with his hips in a special cradle alongside the roaring engine. The cradle could be moved slightly from side to side, and its motion controlled the lateral movement of the machine. In addition, he grasped a small lever which controlled climb or dive.

Wilbur stood on the sand next to the machine holding onto a wing tip to balance it. With the engine racing, Orville slipped the release that had been holding the machine in position and it began to roll forward, with Wilbur walking, then trotting, then running alongside. When he began to stumble, he let go. The first heavier-than-air self-powered flying machine was in the air under the control of a human passenger.

Orville slipped the release, the machine began to roll forward

From the moment the machine started, Orville "found the control of the front rudder quite difficult. . . . (It) had a tendency to turn itself when started so that (it) . . . turned too far on one side and then too far on the other . . ." Because of the rudder, the machine began to dart toward the ground when it had risen only ten feet. Orville got it under control and flew a hundred feet, when suddenly the machine glided down and landed. The time of the first powered flight under human control was twelve seconds. In his diary that day, Orville noted only that the "flight lever for throwing off the engine was broken and the skid under the rudder cracked."

During those twelve seconds, however, Orville was well aware that he was making history, and years later he described his feelings this way: "The motor close beside you kept up an almost deafening roar during the whole flight, yet in your excitement, you did not notice it till it stopped."

Twelve seconds that changed the world

The two brothers spent half an hour dragging the machine back to the track and making the necessary repairs. At eleven o'clock, Wilbur made the second flight. His course was very much like Orville's. The machine flew low and wobbly, rising and falling for 175 feet before it came down to the blowing sand.

The wind was beginning to ease off and, with the aid of the men from the life-saving station, the machine was put back on the track for a third try. At eleven-twenty, Orville took off.

"When out about the same distance as Will, I met with a strong gust from the left which raised the left wing and sidled the machine off to the right in a lively manner. I immediately turned the rudder to bring the machine down, and then worked the end control. Much to our surprise, on reaching the ground the left wing struck first, showing the lateral control of this machine much more effective than on any of our former ones."

Then it was Wilbur's turn

Twenty minutes later it was Wilbur's turn to make the fourth trial. At just twelve, the machine took off, and now it was under much better control. It flew evenly for eight hundred feet, when it began to pitch and suddenly darted to the ground. "The front rudder frame," wrote Orville, "was badly broken up, but the main frame suffered none at all. The distance over the ground was 852 feet in fifty-nine seconds."

The two brothers and their five helpers carried the machine back and set it down on the sand for a few minutes, while Wilbur discussed what had happened in the last flight. Suddenly a gust of wind came up, raised the wing of the machine and started to spin it over. Everyone rushed to hold it down.

"Mr. Daniels, having had no experience in handling a machine of this kind, hung on to it from the inside, and as a result he was knocked down and turned over and over with it as it ran. His escape was miraculous, as he was in with the engine and chains. The engine legs were all broken off, the chain guys badly bent, a number of uprights and nearly all the rear ends of the ribs were badly broken."

A complete reconstruction job was necessary, and

so the two Wright brothers knocked off for lunch, knowing that they were not only the first men to fly in a machine that rose and maintained itself in level flight under its own power, but what was far more important, they were the first men to fly with a complete system of control. For another fifty years these principles, which they had worked out entirely by themselves, were to remain the essential laws of flight control.

They had worked out for themselves the essential laws of flight control

In their shack on the windy dunes, Orville cooked the lunch and Wilbur, as usual, washed the dishes.

* * *

The Wrights felt a glow of pride and satisfaction in having both invented and demonstrated the device that had baffled the ablest scientists through the centuries. But still they did not expect to make their fortunes. True, they had applied, on March 23, 1903, or nearly nine months before they flew, for basic patents (not issued until May 22, 1906), but that was by way of establishing an authentic record. Thus far they hadn't even employed a patent lawyer.

Long afterward, Orville Wright was asked what he and Wilbur would have taken for all their secrets of aviation, for all patent rights *for the entire world,* if someone had come along to talk terms just after those first flights. He wasn't sure, but he had an idea that if they had received an offer of ten thousand dollars they might have accepted it.

After the event

Since the airplane was not yet developed into a type for practical use, ten thousand dollars might have been considered a fair return for their time, effort, and outlay. They had had all the fun and satisfaction and their expenses had been surprisingly small. Their cash outlay for building and flying their power plane was less than $1,000, and that included their railroad fares to and from Kitty

Hawk. Of course, the greater part of their expenses would have been for mechanical labor, much of which they did themselves. But skilled labor was low-priced at that time; one could hire a better than average mechanic for as little as $16 a week. Even if the Wrights had charged themselves with the cost of their own work, their total expenses on the power plane would still have been less than $2,000.

A persistent rumor

Many fanciful stories have been told about the sacrifices the Wright family made to enable the brothers to fly, and of how they were financed by this person or that. More than one man of wealth in Dayton has encouraged the belief that *he* financed them. One persistent story is that they raised money for their experiments by the sale of an Iowa farm in which they had an interest. The truth is that this farm, which had been deeded by their father to the *four* Wright brothers, was sold early in 1902 before Wilbur and Orville had even begun work on their power plane or spent much on their experiments. The sale was made at the request of their brother Reuchlin, and had no relation whatsoever to aviation. Nor is it true that the Wright home was mortgaged during the time of the brothers' experiments. Another story was that their sister Katharine had furnished the money they needed out of her salary as school teacher. Katharine Wright was always amused over that tale, for she was never a hoarder of money nor a financier, and could hardly have provided funds even if this had been necessary. Any rumor that her brothers could have borrowed money from her, rather than lending money to her, as they sometimes did, was almost as funny to Katharine as another report – that her brothers had relied on her for mathematical assistance in their calculations.

The simple fact is that no one ever financed the Wrights' work except Wilbur and Orville themselves. Their bicycle business had been giving them a decent income and at the end of the year 1903 they still had a few thousand dollars' savings in a local building and loan association. Whatever financial scrimping was necessary came *after* they had flown; after they knew they had made a great discovery.

Success was an orphan

But the Wrights' belief that they had achieved something of great importance was not bolstered by the attitude of the general public. Not only were there no receptions, brass bands, or parades in their honor, but most people paid less attention to the history-making feat than if they had simply been on vacation and caught a big fish, or shot a bear.

Before the flights, some of the neighbors had been puzzled by reports that the Wrights were working on a flying machine. One man in business near the Wright shop had become acquainted with an inventor who thought he was about to perfect a perpetual motion machine; and this businessman promptly sent the inventor to the Wrights, assuming that he would find them kindred spirits. John G. Feight, living next door to the Wright home, had remarked, just before the brothers went to Kitty Hawk: "Flying and perpetual motion will come at the same time."

The popular notion of disbelief

Now that flights had been made, neighbors didn't doubt the truth of the reports – though one of them had his own explanation. Mr. Webbert, father of the man from whom the Wrights rented their shop, said: "I have known those boys ever since they were small children, and if they say they flew I know they did; but I think there must be special conditions down in North Carolina that would enable them to fly by the power of a motor. There is only one thing that could lift a machine like that in *this* part of the country – spirit power." Webbert was a spiritualist. He had seen tables and pianos lifted at séances!

But even if the boys *had* flown, what of it? Men were flying in Europe, weren't they? Hadn't Santos-Dumont flown some kind of self-propelled balloon?

The one person who had almost unbounded enthusiasm for what the brothers had accomplished was their father. They found it difficult to keep a complete file of the photographs they had made showing different phases of their experiments, because the moment their father's eye fell on one of these pictures he would pick it up and mail it to some relative along with a letter telling with pride what the boys had done.

Two brothers in Boston sensed, however, that, if the scant reports about the Kitty Hawk event were based on truth, then something of great significance had happened. These men were Samuel and Godfrey Lowell Cabot, wealthy and influential members of a famous family. Both of them, particularly Samuel, had long been interested in whatever progress was being made in aeronautics. On December 19, the day after the first news of the flights was published, Samuel Cabot sent to the Wrights a telegram of congratulations. Two days later, his brother Godfrey wrote them a letter. In that letter Godfrey Cabot wanted to know if they thought their machine could be used for carrying freight. He was financially interested in an industrial operation in West Virginia, he said, where conditions would justify a rate of $10 a ton for transporting goods by air only sixteen miles.

They said it couldn't be done

One reason why nearly everyone in the United States was disinclined to swallow the reports about flying with a machine heavier than air was that important scientists had already explained in the public prints why the thing was impossible. When a man of the profound scientific wisdom of Simon Newcomb, for example, had demonstrated with unassailable logic why man couldn't fly, why should the public be fooled by silly stories about two obscure bicycle repairmen who hadn't even been to college? Professor Newcomb was so distinguished an astronomer that he was the only American since Benjamin Franklin to be made an associate of the Institute of France. It was widely assumed that what he didn't know about laws of physics simply wasn't in books; and that when he said flying couldn't be done, there was no need to inquire any further. More than once Professor Newcomb had written that flight without gasbags would require the discovery of some new metal or a new unsuspected force in nature. Then, in an article in *The Independent*–October 22, 1903, while the Wrights were at Kitty Hawk assembling their power machine–he not only proved that trying to fly was nonsense, but went further and showed that even if a man did fly, he wouldn't dare to stop. "Once he slackens his speed, down he begins to fall. Once he stops, he falls a dead mass. How shall he reach the ground without destroying his delicate machinery? I do not think that even the most imaginative inventor has yet put on paper a demonstrative, successful way of meeting this difficulty."

Defying the laws of nature

In all his statements, Professor Newcomb had the support of other eminent authorities, including Rear Admiral George W. Melville, then chief engineer for the United States Navy, who, a year or two previously, in the *North American Review,* had set forth convincingly the absurdity of attempts to fly.

The most recent Newcomb article was all the more impressive as a forecast from the fact that it appeared only fifteen days after one of Professor Langley's unsuccessful attempts at flight. That is, Langley's attempt seemed to show that flight was beyond human possibility, and then Newcomb's article explained *why* it was impossible. Though these pooh-poohing statements by Newcomb and other scientists were probably read by relatively few people, they were seen by editors, editorial writers, and others who could have much influence on public opinion. Naturally, no editor who *knew* a thing couldn't be done would permit his paper to record the fact that it had been done.

Oddly enough, one of the first public announcements by word of mouth about the Wrights' Kitty Hawk flights was in a Sunday school. A. I. Root, founder of a still prosperous business for the sale of honey and beekeepers' supplies at Medina, Ohio, taught a Sunday-school class. One morning shortly before the dismissal bell, observing that the boys in the class were restless, he sought to restore order by catching their interest. Perhaps he wished to show, too, that miracles as wonderful as any in the Bible were still possible.

"Do you know, friends," he said, "that two Ohio boys, or young men rather, have outstripped the world in demonstrating that a flying machine can be constructed without the aid of a balloon?" He had read a brief item about the Wrights in an Akron newspaper.

A credit to our country

The class became attentive and Root went on: "During the past two months these two boys have made a machine that actually flew through the air for more than half a mile, carrying one of the boys with it. This young man is not only a credit to our state but to the whole country and to the world."

Though this was several weeks after the Wrights had first flown, no one in the class had ever heard about it, and incredulously they fired questions at the teacher.

"Where do the boys live? What are their names? When and where did their machine fly?"

Root described, not too accurately, the Kitty Hawk flights, and added: "When they make their next trial I am going to try to be on hand to see the experiment."

An important part of Root's business was publication of the still widely circulated magazine, *Gleanings in Bee Culture,* and in his issue of March 1, 1904, he told of the episode in the Sunday school. By printing that story, the Medina bee man may possibly have been the first editor of a scientific publication in the United States to report that man could fly. (The *Popular Science Monthly* in its issue of March, 1904, had an article by Octave Chanute in which the flights were mentioned.) Root a little later even predicted: "Possibly we may be able to fly over the North Pole."

The Wrights were more amused than disturbed by the lack of general recognition that flying was now possible. They inwardly chuckled when they heard people still using the old expression: "Why, a person could no more do *that* than he could fly!" But they knew they had only begun to learn about handling a flying machine.

* * *

Epilogue

In a corner of the Pullman smoking compartment, by the window, the man who had been explaining the whole economic system mentioned inventors as an example of the fortunate relationship between desire for money and scientific progress.

"Take the Wright brothers," he said. "Would they have worked all those years trying to fly just for their health?"

Another passenger ventured to ask: "Don't people sometimes become curious about a problem and work to see what they can find out?"

The man by the window chuckled tolerantly as he

replied: "Do you think those Wright brothers would have kept on pouring money into their experiments and risking their lives if they hadn't hoped to get rich at it? No, sir! It was the chance to make a fortune that kept them going." Most other passengers in the compartment nodded in agreement.

Not long afterward, one of those who had overheard that conversation was in Dayton, Ohio, and inquired of his friend Orville Wright: "Do you think the expectation of profit is the main incentive to inventors?"

Orville Wright didn't think so. He doubted if Alexander Graham Bell expected to make much out of the telephone. And it seemed to him unlikely that Edison started out with the idea of making money. Certainly, he said, Steinmetz had little interest in financial reward. All Steinmetz asked of life was the opportunity to spend as much time as possible in the laboratory working at problems that interested him.

"And the Wright brothers?"

If they had been interested in invention with the idea of making money, said Orville Wright, looking amused, they "most assuredly would have tried something in which the chances for success were brighter."

Innovation & Achievement

1908

Henry Ford

9

Anything that is good for only a few people is really no good. It's got to be good for everybody or in the end it will not survive.

In his own words

My "gasoline buggy" was the first and for a long time the only automobile in Detroit. It was considered to be something of a nuisance, for it made a racket and it scared horses. Also it blocked traffic. For if I stopped my machine anywhere in town a crowd was around it before I could start up again. If I left it alone even for a minute some inquisitive person always tried to run it. Finally, I had to carry a chain and chain it to a lamppost whenever I left it anywhere. And then there was trouble with the police. I do not know quite why, for my impression is that there were no speed limit laws in those days. Anyway, I had to get a special permit from the mayor and thus for a time enjoyed the distinction of being the only licensed chauffeur in America. I ran that machine about one thousand miles through 1895 and 1896 and then sold it to Charles Ainsley of Detroit for two hundred dollars. That was my first sale. I had built the car not to sell but only to experiment with. I wanted to start another car. Ainsley wanted to buy. I could use the money, and we had no trouble in agreeing upon a price.

It was not at all my idea to make cars in any such

It was not my idea to make cars in a petty fashion

petty fashion. I was looking ahead to production, but before that could come I had to have something to produce. It does not pay to hurry. I started a second car in 1896; it was much like the first but a little lighter. It also had the belt drive which I did not give up until some time later; the belts were all right excepting in hot weather. That is why I later adopted gears. I learned a great deal from that car. Others in this country and abroad were building cars by that time, and in 1895 I heard that a Benz car from Germany was on exhibition in Macy's store in New York. I traveled down to look at it but it had no features that seemed worthwhile. It also had the belt drive, but it was much heavier than my car. I was working for lightness. I built three cars in all in my home shop and all of them ran for years in Detroit.

During all this time I kept my position with the electric company and gradually advanced to chief engineer at a salary of one hundred and twenty-five dollars a month. But my gas engine experiments were no more popular with the president of the company than my first mechanical leanings were with my father. It was not that my employer objected to experiments–only to experiments with a gas engine. I can still hear him say: "Electricity, yes, that's the coming thing. But gas–no."

Practically no one had the remotest notion of the future possibilities

He had ample grounds for his skepticism–to use the mildest terms. Practically no one had the remotest notion of the future of the internal combustion engine, while we were just on the edge of the great electrical development. As with every comparatively new idea, electricity was expected to do much more than we even now have any indication that it can do. I did not see the use of experimenting with electricity for my purposes. A road car could not run on a trolley even if trolley wires had been less expensive; no storage battery was in sight of a weight that was practical. An electrical car had of necessity to be limited in radius and to contain a large amount of motive machinery in proportion to the power.

The Edison Company offered me the general superintendency of the company but only on condition that I would give up my gas engine and devote myself to something really useful. I had to choose between my job and my automobile. I chose the automobile, or rather I gave up the job – there was really nothing in the way of a choice. For already I knew that the car was bound to be a success. I quit my job on August 15, 1899, and went into the automobile business.

I quit my job and took a chance

It might be thought something of a step, for I had no personal funds. What money was left over from living was all used in experimenting. But my wife agreed that the automobile could not be given up – that we had to make or break. There was no *demand* for automobiles – there never is for a new article. They were accepted in much the fashion as was more recently the airplane. At first the "horseless carriage" was considered merely a freak notion and many wise people explained with particularity why it could never be more than a toy. No man of money even thought of it as a commercial possibility.

In the beginning there was hardly any one who sensed that the automobile could be a large factor in industry. The most optimistic hoped only for a development akin to that of the bicycle. When it was found that an automobile really could go and several makers started to put out cars, the immediate query was as to which would go fastest. It was a curious but natural development – that racing idea. I never thought anything of racing, but the public refused to consider the automobile in any light other than as a fast toy. Therefore later we had to race. The industry was held back by this initial racing slant, for the attention of the makers was diverted to making fast rather than good cars. It was a business for speculators.

It was a business for speculators

A group of men of speculative turn of mind organized, as soon as I left the electric company, the Detroit Automobile Company to exploit my car. I was the chief engineer and held a small amount of the stock. For three years we continued making cars more or less on the model of my first car. We sold very few of them; I could get no support at all toward making better cars to be sold to the public at large. The whole thought was to make to order and to get the largest price possible for each car. The main idea seemed to be to get the money. And being without authority other than my engineering position gave me, I found that the new company was not a vehicle for realizing my ideas but merely a money-making concern–that did not make much money. In March, 1902, I resigned, determined never again to put myself under orders. The Detroit Automobile Company later became the Cadillac Company under the ownership of the Lelands, who came in subsequently.

I rented a one-story brick shed

I rented a shop–a one-story brick shed–at 81 Park Place to continue my experiments and to find out what business really was. I thought that it must be something different from what it had proved to be in my first adventure.

The year from 1902 until the formation of the Ford Motor Company was practically one of investigation. In my little one room brick shop I worked on the development of a four-cylinder motor and on the outside I tried to find out what business really was and whether it needed to be quite so selfish a scramble for money as it seemed to be from my first short experience. From the period of the first car, which I have described, until the formation of my company I built in all about twenty-five cars, of which nineteen or twenty were built with the Detroit Automobile Company. The automobile had passed from the initial stage where the fact that it could run at all was enough, to the stage where it had to show speed. Alexander Winton of Cleveland, the founder of the Winton car, was then the track champion of the country and willing to meet all comers. I designed a two-cylinder enclosed engine of a more compact type than I had before used, fitted it into a skeleton chassis, found that I could make speed, and arranged a race with Winton. We met on the Grosse Point track at Detroit. I beat him. That was my first race, and it brought advertising of the only kind that people cared to read.

People wanted speed – I gave them what they wanted

The public thought nothing of a car unless it made speed – unless it beat other racing cars. My ambition to build the fastest car in the world led me to plan a four-cylinder motor.

The idea in those days was that a first class car ought to be a racer. I never really thought much of racing, but following the bicycle idea, the manufacturers had the notion that winning a race on a track told the public something about the merits of an automobile – although I can hardly imagine any test that would tell less.

But, as the others were doing it, I, too, had to do it. In 1903, with Tom Cooper, I built two cars solely for speed. They were quite alike. One we named the "999" and the other the "Arrow." If an automobile were going to be known for speed, then I was going to make an automobile that would be known wherever speed was known. These were. I put in four great big cylinders giving 80 H.P. – which up to that time had been unheard of. The roar of those cylinders alone was enough to half kill a man. There was only one seat. One life to a car was enough. I tried out the cars. Cooper tried out the cars. We let them out at full speed. I cannot quite describe the sensation. Going over Niagara Falls would have been but a pastime after a ride in one of them. I did not want to take the responsibility of racing the "999" which we put up first, neither did Cooper. Cooper said he knew a man who lived on speed, that nothing could go too fast for him. He wired to Salt Lake City and on came a professional bicycle rider named Barney Oldfield. He had never driven a motor car, but he liked the idea of trying it. He said he would try anything once.

Barney Oldfield helped me do it

It took us only a week to teach him how to drive. The man did not know what fear was. All that he had to learn was how to control the monster. Controlling the fastest car of today was nothing as compared to controlling that car. The steering wheel had not yet been thought of. All the previous cars that I had built simply had tillers. On this one I put a two-handed tiller, for holding the car in line required all the strength of a strong man. The race for which we were working was at three miles on the Grosse Point track. We kept our cars as a dark horse. We left the predictions to the others. The tracks then were not scientifically banked. It was not known how much speed a motor car could develop. No one knew better than Oldfield what the turns meant and as he took his seat, while I was cranking the car for the start, he remarked cheerily: "This chariot may kill me, but they will say afterward that I was going like hell when she took me over the bank."

And he did go. . . . He never dared to look around. He did not shut off on the curves. He simply let that car go–and go it did. He was about half a mile ahead of the next man at the end of the race!

The "999" did what it was intended to do: It advertised the fact that I could build a fast motor car. A week after the race I formed the Ford Motor Company. I was vice president, designer, master mechanic, superintendent, and general manager. The capitalization of the company was one hundred thousand dollars, and of this I owned 25½ percent. The total amount subscribed in cash was about twenty-eight thousand dollars—which is the only money that the company has ever received for the capital fund from other than operations.

A week after the race, I formed the Ford Motor Company

In the beginning I thought that it was possible, notwithstanding my former experience, to go forward with a company in which I owned less than the controlling share. I very shortly found I had to have control and therefore in 1906, with funds that I had earned in the company, I bought enough stock to bring my holdings up to 51 percent, and a little later bought enough more to give me 58½ percent. In 1919 my son Edsel purchased the remaining 41½ percent of the stock because certain of the minority stockholders disagreed with my policies. For these shares he paid at the rate of $12,500 for each $100 par and in all paid about seventy-five million.

The original company and its equipment, as may be gathered, were not elaborate. We rented Strelow's carpenter shop on Mack Avenue. In making my designs I had also worked out the methods of making, but, since at that time we could not afford to buy machinery, the entire car was made according to my designs, but by various manufacturers, and about all we did, even in the way of assembling, was to put on the wheels, the tires, and the body.

We rented a carpenter shop on Mack Avenue

I had been experimenting principally upon the cutting down of weight. Excess weight kills any self-propelled vehicle. There are a lot of fool ideas about weight.

Strength has nothing to do with weight

For some clumsy reason we have come to confuse strength with weight. The crude methods of early building undoubtedly had much to do with this. The old ox cart weighed a ton—and it had so much weight that it was weak! To carry a few tons of humanity from New York to Chicago, the railroad builds a train that weighs many hundred tons, and the result is an absolute loss of real strength and the extravagant waste of untold millions in the form of power. The law of diminishing returns begins to operate at the point where strength becomes weight. Weight may be desirable in a steamroller but nowhere else. Strength has nothing to do with weight. The mentality of the man who does things in the world is agile, light, and strong. The most beautiful things in the world are those from which all excess weight has been eliminated. Strength is never just weight—either in men or things. Whenever any one suggests to me that I might increase weight or add a part, I look into decreasing weight and eliminating a part! The car that I designed was lighter than any car that had yet been made. It would have been lighter if I had known how to make it so—later I got the materials to make the lighter car.

In our first year we built "Model A," selling the runabout for eight hundred and fifty dollars and the tonneau for one hundred dollars more. This model had a two-cylinder opposed motor developing eight horsepower. It had a chain drive, a seventy-two inch wheel base—which was supposed to be long—and a fuel capacity of five gallons. We made and sold 1,708 cars in the first year. That is how well the public responded.

Our cars gained a reputation for standing up

The business went along almost as by magic. The cars gained a reputation for standing up. They were tough, they were simple, and they were well made. I was working on my design for a universal single model but I had not settled the designs nor had we the money to build and equip the proper kind of plant for manufacturing. I had not the money to discover the very best and lightest materials. We still had to accept the materials that the market offered – we got the best to be had but we had no facilities for the scientific investigation of materials or for original research.

In the second year we scattered our energies among three models. We made a four-cylinder touring car, "Model B," which sold for $2,000; "Model C," which was a slightly improved "Model A" and sold at fifty dollars more than the former price; and "Model F," a touring car which sold for $1,000. That is, we scattered our energy and increased prices – and therefore we sold fewer cars than in the first year. The sales were 1,695 cars.

Winning a race is the best kind of advertising

That "Model B" – the first four-cylinder car for general road use – had to be advertised. Winning a race or making a record was then the best kind of advertising. So I fixed up the "Arrow," the twin of the old "999" – in fact practically remade it – and a week before the New York Automobile show I drove it myself over a surveyed mile straightaway on the ice. I shall never forget that race. The ice seemed smooth enough, so smooth that if I had called off the trial we should have secured an immense amount of the wrong kind of advertising, but instead of being smooth, that ice was seamed with fissures which I knew were going to mean trouble the moment I got up speed. But there was nothing to do but go through with the trial, and I let the old "Arrow" out. At every fissure the car leaped into the air. I never knew how it was coming down. When I wasn't in the air, I was skidding, but somehow I stayed top side up and on the course, making a record that went all over the world! That put "Model

B" on the map – but not enough on to overcome the price advances. No stunt and no advertising will sell an article for any length of time. Business is not a game.

We began to make and assemble parts

Our little wooden shop had, with the business we were doing, become totally inadequate, and in 1906 we took out of our working capital sufficient funds to build a three-story plant at the corner of Piquette and Beaubien streets – which for the first time gave us real manufacturing facilities. We began to make and to assemble quite a number of the parts, although still we were principally an assembling shop. In 1905-1906 we made only two models – one the four-cylinder car at $2,000 and another touring car at $1,000, both being the models of the previous year – and our sales dropped to 1,599 cars.

Some said it was because we had not brought out new models. I thought it was because our cars were too expensive. I changed the policy in the next year – having first acquired stock control. For 1906-1907 we entirely left off making touring cars and made three models of runabouts and roadsters, none of which differed materially from the other in manufacturing process or in component parts, but were somewhat different in appearance. The big thing was that the cheapest car sold for $600 and the most expensive for only $750, and right there came the complete demonstration of what price meant. We sold 8,423 cars – nearly five times as many as in our biggest previous year. Our banner week was that of May 15, 1908, when we assembled 311 cars in six working days. It almost swamped our facilities. The foreman had a tallyboard on which he chalked up each car as it was finished and turned over to the testers. The tallyboard was hardly equal to the task. On one day in the following June we assembled an even one hundred cars.

The next year we departed from the program that had been so successful and I designed a big car—fifty horsepower, six cylinder—that would burn up the roads. We continued making our small cars, but the 1907 panic and the diversion to the more expensive model cut down the sales to 6,398 cars.

We experimented for five years

We had been through an experimenting period of five years. The cars were beginning to be sold in Europe. The business, as an automobile business then went, was considered extraordinarily prosperous. We had plenty of money. We sold for cash, we did not borrow money, and we sold directly to the purchaser. We had no bad debts, and we kept within ourselves on every move.

The way was not easy. We were harried by a big suit brought against the company to try to force us into line with an association of automobile manufacturers, who were operating under the false principle that there was only a limited market for automobiles and that a monopoly of that market was essential. This was the famous Selden Patent suit. The situation was this:

George B. Selden, a patent attorney, filed an application as far back as 1879 for a patent the object of which was stated to be "The production of a safe, simple, and cheap road locomotive, light in weight, easy to control, possessed of sufficient power to overcome an ordinary inclination." This application was kept alive in the Patent Office, by methods which are perfectly legal, until 1895, when the patent was granted. In 1879, when the application was filed, the automobile was practically unknown to the general public, but by the time the patent was issued everybody was familiar with self-propelled vehicles, and most of the men, including myself, who had been for years working on motor propulsion, were surprised to learn that what we had made practicable was covered by an application of years before, although the applicant had kept his idea merely as an idea. He had done nothing to put it into practice.

The specific claims under the patent were divided into six groups, and I think that not a single one of them was a really new idea even in 1879 when the application was filed. The Patent Office allowed a combination and issued a so-called "combination patent" deciding that the combination (a) of a carriage with its body machinery and steering wheel, with the (b) propelling mechanism clutch and gear, and finally (c) the engine, made a valid patent.

Other manufacturers rallied against us

With all of that we were not concerned. I believed that my engine had nothing whatsoever in common with what Selden had in mind. The powerful combination of manufacturers who called themselves the "licensed manufacturers" because they operated under licenses from the patentee, brought suit against us as soon as we began to be a factor in motor production. The suit dragged on. It was intended to scare us out of business. We took volumes of testimony, and the blow came on September 15, 1909, when Judge Hough rendered an opinion in the United States District Court finding against us. Immediately that Licensed Association began to advertise, warning prospective purchasers against our cars. They had done the same thing in 1903 at the start of the suit, when it was thought that we could be put out of business. I had implicit confidence that eventually we should win our suit. I simply knew that we were right, but it was a considerable blow to get the first decision against us, for we believed that many buyers—even though no injunction was issued against us—would be frightened away from buying because of the threats of court action against individual owners. The idea was spread that if the suit finally went against me, every man who owned a Ford car would be prosecuted. Some of my more enthusiastic opponents, I understand, gave it out privately that there would be criminal as well as civil suits and that a man buying a Ford car might as well be buying a ticket to jail. We answered with a four-page advertisement in the principal newspapers all over the country.

In 1905 I was at a motor race at Palm Beach. There was a big smashup and a French car was wrecked. We had entered our "Model K"–the high-powered six. I thought the foreign cars had smaller and better parts than we knew anything about. After the wreck I picked up a little valve strip stem. It was very light and very strong. I asked what it was made of. Nobody knew. I gave the stem to my assistant.

I discovered a unique, competitive advantage

"Find out all about this," I told him. "That is the kind of material we ought to have in our cars."

He found eventually that it was a French steel and that there was vanadium in it. We tried every steel maker in America–not one could make vanadium steel. I sent to England for a man who understood how to make the steel commercially. The next thing was to get a plant to turn it out. That was another problem. Vanadium requires 3,000 degrees Fahrenheit. The ordinary furnace could not go beyond 2,700 degrees. I found a small steel company in Canton, Ohio. I offered to guarantee them against loss if they would run a heat for us. They agreed. The first heat was a failure. Very little vanadium remained in the steel. I had them try again, and the second time the steel came through. Until then we had been forced to be satisfied with steel running between 60,000 and 70,000 pounds tensile strength. With vanadium, the tensile strength went up to 170,000 pounds.

Having vanadium in hand I pulled apart our models and tested in detail to determine what kind of steel was best for every part – whether we wanted a hard steel, a tough steel, or an elastic steel. We, for the first time I think, in the history of any large construction, determined scientifically the exact quality of the steel. As a result we then selected twenty different types of steel for the various steel parts. About ten of these were vanadium. Vanadium was used wherever strength and lightness were required. Of course they are not all the same kind of vanadium steel. The other elements vary according to whether the part is to stand hard wear or whether it needs spring – in short, according to what it needs. Before these experiments I believe that not more than four different grades of steel had ever been used in automobile construction. By further experimenting, especially in the direction of heat treating, we were able still further to increase the strength of the steel and therefore to reduce the weight of the car. In 1910 the French Department of Commerce and Industry took one of our steering spindle connecting rod yokes – selecting it as a vital unit – and tried it against a similar part from what they considered the best French car, and in every test our steel proved the stronger.

Increasing strength, reducing weight

The vanadium steel disposed of much of the weight. The other requisites of a universal car I had already worked out and many of them were in practice. The design had to balance. Men die because a part gives out. Machines wreck themselves because some parts are weaker than others. Therefore, a part of the problem in designing a universal car was to have as nearly as possible all parts of equal strength considering their purpose – to put a motor in a one-horse shay. Also it had to be foolproof. This was difficult because a gasoline motor is essentially a delicate instrument and there is a wonderful opportunity for any one who has a mind that way to mess it up. I adopted this slogan: "When one of my cars breaks down I know I am to blame."

From the day the first motor car appeared on the streets it had to me appeared to be a necessity. It was this knowledge and assurance that led me to build to the one end – a car that would meet the wants of the multitudes. The universal car had to have these attributes:

The attributes of the universal car

(1) Quality in material to give service in use. Vanadium steel is the strongest, toughest, and most lasting of steels. It forms the foundation and superstructure of the cars. It is the highest quality steel in this respect in the world, regardless of price.

(2) Simplicity in operation – because the masses are not mechanics.

(3) Power in sufficient quantity.

(4) Absolute reliability – because of the varied uses to which the cars would be put and the variety of roads over which they would travel.

(5) Lightness. With the Ford there are only 7.95 pounds to be carried by each cubic inch of piston displacement. This is one of the reasons why Ford cars are "always going," wherever and whenever you see them – through sand and mud, through slush, snow, and water, up hills, across fields and roadless plains.

(6) Control – to hold its speed always in hand, calmly and safely meeting every emergency and contingency either in the crowded streets of the city or on dangerous roads. The planetary transmission of the Ford gave this control and anybody could work it. That is the *why* of the saying: "Anybody can drive a Ford."

(7) The more a motor car weighs, naturally the more fuel and lubricants are used in the driving; the lighter the weight the lighter the expense of operation. The light weight of the Ford car in its early

years was used as an argument against it. Now that is all changed.

The design which I settled upon was called "Model T." The important feature of the new model – which, if it were accepted, as I thought it would be, I intended to make the only model and then start into real production – was its simplicity. There were but four constructional units in the car – the power plant, the frame, the front axle, and the rear axle. All of these were easily accessible and they were designed so that no special skill would be required for their repair or replacement. I believed then, although I said very little about it because of the novelty of the idea, that it ought to be possible to have parts so simple and so inexpensive that the menace of expensive hand repair work would be entirely eliminated. The parts could be made so cheaply that it would be less expensive to buy new ones than to have old ones repaired. They could be carried in hardware shops just as nails or bolts are carried. I thought that it was up to me as the designer to make the car so completely simple that no one could fail to understand it.

Hardware stores carried our parts

The "Model T" had practically no features which were not contained in some one or other of the previous models. Every detail had been fully tested in practice. There was no guessing as to whether or not it would be a successful model. It had to be. There was no way it could escape being so, for it had not been made in a day. It contained all that I was then able to put into a motor car plus the material, which for the first time I was able to obtain. We put out "Model T" for the season 1908-1909.

* * *

Henry Ford, one of the world's best known industrialists, wielded an extraordinary influence on the

American scene. His Model T, mass production methods, and wage-price theories revolutionized American industry and reverberated around the world. An indigenous folk hero, Ford appealed to millions of his countrymen because, in their view, he succeeded through his own creativeness and hard work and by supplying a product to meet the public's desires rather than by manipulating money or people. He also was admired, despite his great wealth, for having retained the common touch. Asked on his fiftieth birthday to cite the greatest handicap of the rich, he replied, "For me, it was when Mrs. Ford stopped cooking." Regarded as an industrial superman and believed by many to typify American civilization and genius, he reminded people of an earlier, simpler society.

Ford was a late starter; life for him began at forty. Born in 1863, he was unknown outside of Detroit until 1901, when his racing exploits placed his name on sports pages. He made two false starts as an auto manufacturer before founding the Ford Motor Company in 1903. Within a decade he had acquired wealth, had become the auto industry's dominant figure, and gained a measure of national prominence. In 1914, at age fifty-one, he became an overnight international celebrity by more than doubling the wages of most of his workers. Ford's prime extended into his late sixties, and perhaps would have lasted longer had it not been for the Great Depression of the 1930s. Even so, the auto maker remained vigorous and continued to guide and personify his company even in his eighties.

How will Ford be regarded in the twenty-first century or 1,000 years from now? Niven Busch, Jr., writing in 1930, suggested that "if it were possible to preserve alive, for the interests of history, one man from each century and country – not, of course, the best or wisest, but the one who represented most thoroughly the hopes, crudities, background, and achievements of his place – no one could better represent this time and the United States than Henry Ford." General Motors' great inventor, Charles F. Kettering, observed in 1943 that "a thousand years from now, when the Churchills and the Roosevelts are but footnotes in history, Henry Ford will loom as the most significant figure of our age." Ford's future reputation rests not only on his achievements, but on future value systems as well. The auto king played a key role in putting the nation on wheels and providing greater abundance for millions.

Innovation & Achievement

1953

James D. Watson

10

Suddenly I realized the potentially profound implications of a DNA structure. Had we found the secret of life?

Commentary by Sir Lawrence Bragg

This account of the events which led to the solution of the structure of DNA, the fundamental genetical material, is unique in several ways.

There is in the first place its scientific interest. The discovery of the structure by Crick and Watson, with all its biological implications, has been one of the major scientific events of the century. The number of researches which it has inspired is amazing; it has caused an explosion in biochemistry which has transformed the science. I have been amongst those who have pressed the author to write his recollections while they are still fresh in his mind, knowing how important they would be as a contribution to the history of science. The result has exceeded expectation. The story, in which the birth of the new idea is described so vividly, is drama of the highest order; the tension mounts and mounts towards where one is able to share so intimately in the researcher's struggles and doubts and final triumph.

Then again, the story is a poignant example of a dilemma which may confront an investigator. He knows that a colleague has been working for years on a problem and has accumulated a mass of hard-won evidence, which has not yet been published because it is anticipated that success is just around the corner. He has seen this evidence and has good reason to believe that a method of attack which he can envisage, perhaps merely a new point of view, will lead straight to the solution. An offer of collaboration at such a stage might well be regarded as a trespass. Should he go ahead on his own?

It is not easy to be sure whether the crucial new idea is really one's own or has been unconsciously assimilated in talks with others. The realization of this difficulty has led to the establishment of a somewhat vague code amongst scientists which recognizes a claim in a line of research staked out by a colleague – up to a certain point.

When competition comes from more than one quarter, there is no need to hold back. This dilemma comes out clearly in the DNA story. It is a source of deep satisfaction to all intimately concerned that, in the award of the Nobel Prize in 1962, due recognition was given to the long, patient investigation by Wilkins at King's College (London) as well as to the brilliant and rapid final solution by Crick and Watson at Cambridge.

Finally, there is the human interest of the story – the impression made by Europe and by England in particular upon a young man from the States.

* * *

Extract from "Threads of Life," by Aaron E. Klein

The evidence that DNA was the stuff of which the gene is made was very strong. If this was the case, the inevitable question loomed – How does DNA act as the genetic material? Before anything could be learned about DNA's possible genetic activity, more had to be learned about the structure of this giant molecule. Biochemists began working on the chemical structure of the nucleic acid. Many of these biochemists, such as Linus Pauling, were well known. Others were hardly known at all, except by their immediate friends and family. Among the latter group were a young American named James Watson and an almost-as-young Englishman named Francis Crick. Common interest in DNA had brought them together at Cambridge University in England in 1951.

Watson had become interested in DNA when he was working for his Ph.D. at Indiana University. His major work had been with bacteriophages. His professor, the microbiologist Salvador Luria, advised Watson that if he expected to find out much about DNA he would have to beef up an extensive inacquaintance with biochemistry. To that end, Watson obtained a grant of money to study the biochemistry of nucleic acids with Hermal Kalckar in Copenhagen.

Many geneticists and biochemists did not seem to realize the significance of DNA

Watson was well aware of the genetic possibilities of DNA. He was amazed that in the early 1950s, there were still many geneticists and biochemists who did not seem to realize DNA's significance. Unfortunately Kalckar was more interested in the metabolism of DNA than its possible genetic significance. Failure to see the wider possibilities is unfortunately a frequent problem with scientists who become intensely involved with the details of their own work.

At a meeting of biologists in Naples, Italy, Watson found out more about methods of studying DNA. At this meeting, he met Maurice Wilkins who was studying DNA with the technique of x-ray crystallography. This technique involved passing x-rays through molecules of crystalline substances. X-rays were passed through a sample of the substance and directed onto photographic film. When the film was developed, characteristic patterns were seen on the resulting picture. The patterns were clues to the structure of the molecule. Interpretation of the patterns could give the investigator an idea of how the atoms were arranged in the molecules.

Watson knew less about x-ray crystallography than he knew about biochemistry. He arranged to go to Cambridge to study x-ray crystallography with Max Perutz, one of the leading experts in x-ray crystallography. When Watson arrived at Cambridge, it did not take him long to find Crick. Informal conversation soon revealed common interests. Their decision to work on DNA was complicated by the fact that Maurice Wilkins was working on the same problem. Both Wilkins and Crick had been physicists and had worked with x-rays. Linus Pauling was also known to be working with DNA in the United States. Finding the structure of DNA soon became a race between Pauling, Wilkins, and the team of Watson and Crick. At the time, if anyone had cared to make a bet on who would be first, the wise gambler would have put his money on Pauling. Pauling had established a reputation as the world's leading biochemist.

The wise gambler would have put his money on Pauling to be first

Soon after Watson came to Cambridge, Pauling published the results of some work he had been doing on the structure of proteins. Pauling, working with sections of proteins called polypeptides, had determined that they were arranged in a helix. A helix is similar to, but not exactly, a spiral. The diameter of a spiral varies at different levels according to a geometric ratio. The diameter of a helix is the same at any point of observation. Pauling had arrived at the alpha helix by constructing a model of the molecule out of objects which resemble children's construction toys. Using what was known about the way atoms came together, and a liberal application of common sense, he had arrived at the alpha helix, for which he received a Nobel Prize.

Watson and Crick felt that they could arrive at the structure of DNA with the same model-building technique. X-ray crystallography pictures would provide them with much of the information they needed to construct their model. When they learned that Pauling had requested some DNA x-ray pictures from Wilkins, they knew that Pauling was working on DNA. Wilkins thought of an excuse not to send the pictures. But Watson and Crick still thought it best to hurry up with their own work.

Watson and Crick thought it best to hurry their own work

X-ray pictures of DNA had indicated that the molecule had a helical structure. The x-ray pictures did not reveal how many strands of atoms the helix had or which atoms were inside or outside the helix.

Some work done by a biochemist named Erwin Chargaff provided Watson and Crick with more information. Chargaff had analyzed DNA from various organisms. DNA had been found in the nuclei of the cells of all organisms which had been analyzed.

Chargaff found that, in all samples of DNA, the amount of adenine always equaled the amount of thymine and the amount of guanine always equaled the amount of cytosine. These data suggested a consistency in structure of the DNA of all organisms. However, if it was DNA which determined the particular characteristics of an organism, then the DNA of different organisms had to differ in some way. Otherwise, if DNA was indeed the genetic stuff, all living things would look exactly the same.

Watson was very much impressed by the work of Hershey and Chase which demonstrated that it was the DNA and not the protein portion of viruses that entered bacteria. This work provided very strong evidence that DNA was the genetic material. This news encouraged the two men to greater efforts. They were probably fully aware that the work of

Hershey and Chase would also spur the other DNA workers to greater efforts.

Watson and Crick decided to use Pauling's model-building techniques. They gathered together all the available material for constructing models of molecules. What other hardware they needed, they had made in the university machine shop. Molecule models are basically balls and sticks or other items which represent atoms and the bonding forces which hold the atoms together. Of course, a good deal more was known about how atoms fit together into molecules than was known in Miescher's time. Even though Watson was no biochemist, he had much more biochemical knowledge than Miescher could have ever obtained in his lifetime.

The pieces of metal, sticks, wire, and other items which went into the model could not be put together in just any way. The model had to conform to what was known about angles, distances, and other relationships between the atoms. The job was complicated by certain atoms which could fit into the molecule in any number of ways.

Slowly a picture of the molecule began to emerge but a major problem remained

Slowly a picture of the molecule began to emerge from the model making. X-ray crystallography data indicated that the molecule was helical. A combination of hunch and various data led Watson and Crick to believe that DNA was a double helix rather than a single one. The outer part of "backbone" of the helix was seen to be composed of alternating units of ribose and phosphate groups. The two strands of ribose-phosphate twisted about each other. X-ray data had given them an idea of the diameter of the helix.

Now they had to fit in the purines and pyrimidines. It appeared that the purines and pyrimidines were inside the helix, attached to the sugar molecules. There was room for two nitrogenous bases between opposite sugars. Two purines were too big to fit inside the helix formed by the two twisted sugar-phosphate strands. Two pyrimidines were too small. A purine and a pyrimidine together fit perfectly. Chargaff's data implied that adenine paired with thymine and guanine paired with cytosine.

There remained the problem of what held the purines and pyrimidines together.

* * *

James Watson's own account of the discovery

My doodling of the bases on paper at first got nowhere, regardless of whether or not I had been to a film. Even the necessity to expunge *Ecstasy* from my mind did not lead to passable hydrogen bonds, and I fell asleep hoping that an undergraduate party the next afternoon at Downing would be full of pretty girls. But my expectations were dashed as soon as I arrived to spot a group of healthy hockey players and several pallid debutantes. Bertrand also instantly perceived he was out of place, and as we passed a polite interval before scooting out, I explained how I was racing Peter's father for the Nobel Prize.

Not until the middle of the next week, however, did a nontrivial idea emerge. It came while I was drawing the fused rings of adenine on paper. Suddenly I realized the potentially profound implications of a DNA structure in which the adenine residue formed hydrogen bonds similar to those found in crystals of pure adenine. If DNA was like this, each adenine residue would form two hydrogen bonds to an adenine residue related to it by a 180-degree rotation. Most important, two symmetrical hydrogen bonds could also hold together pairs of guanine, cytosine, or thymine. I thus started wondering whether each DNA molecule consisted of two chains with identical base sequences held together by hydrogen bonds between pairs of identical bases. There was the complication, however, that such a structure could not have a regular backbone, since the purines (adenine and guanine) and the pyrimidines (thymine and cytosine) have different shapes. The resulting backbone would have to show minor in-and-out buckles depending upon whether pairs of purines or pyrimidines were in the center.

My pulse began to race

Despite the messy backbone, my pulse began to race. If this was DNA, I should create a bombshell by announcing its discovery. The existence of two intertwined chains with identical base sequences could not be a chance matter. Instead it would strongly suggest that one chain in each molecule had at some earlier stage served as the template for the synthesis of the other chain. Under this scheme, gene replication starts with the separation of its two identical chains. Then two new daughter strands are made on the two parental templates, thereby forming two DNA molecules identical to the original molecule. Thus, the essential trick of gene replication could come from the requirement that each base in the newly synthesized chain always hydrogen-bonds to an identical base. That night, however, I could not see why the common tautomeric form of guanine would not hydrogen-bond to adenine. Likewise, several other pairing mistakes should also occur. But since there was no reason to rule out the participation of specific enzymes, I saw no need to be unduly disturbed. For example, there might exist an enzyme specific for adenine that caused adenine always to be inserted opposite an adenine residue on the template strands.

As the clock went past midnight I was becoming more and more pleased. There had been far too many days when Francis and I worried that the DNA structure might turn out to be superficially very dull, suggesting nothing about either its replication or its function in controlling cell biochemistry. But now, to my delight and amazement, the answer was turning out to be profoundly interesting. For over two hours I happily lay awake with pairs of adenine residues whirling in front of my closed eyes. Only for brief moments did the fear shoot through me that an idea this good could be wrong.

As the clock went past midnight I was becoming more pleased

My scheme was torn to shreds by the following noon. Against me was the awkward chemical fact that I had chosen the wrong tautomeric forms of guanine and thymine. Before the disturbing truth came out, I had eaten a hurried breakfast at the Whim, then momentarily gone back to Clare to reply to a letter from Max Delbrück which reported that my manuscript on bacterial genetics looked unsound to the Cal Tech geneticists. Nevertheless, he would accede to my request that he send it to the *Proceedings of the National Academy*. In this way, I would still be young when I committed the folly of publishing a silly idea. Then I could sober up before my career was permanently fixed on a reckless course.

At first this message had its desired unsettling effect. But now, with my spirits soaring on the possibility that I had the self-duplicating structure, I reiterated my faith that I knew what happened when bacteria mated. Moreover, I could not refrain from adding a sentence saying that I had just devised a beautiful DNA structure which was completely different from Pauling's. For a few seconds I considered giving some details of what I was up to, but since I was in a rush I decided not to, quickly dropped the letter in the box, and dashed to the lab.

The letter was not in the post for more than an hour before I knew that my claim was nonsense. I no sooner got to the office and began explaining my scheme than the American crystallographer Jerry Donohue protested that the idea would not work.

Though my immediate reaction was to hope that Jerry was blowing hot air, I did not dismiss his criticism. Next to Linus himself, Jerry knew more about hydrogen bonds than anyone else in the world. Since for many years he had worked at Cal Tech on the crystal structures of small organic molecules, I couldn't kid myself that he did not grasp our problem. During the six months that he occupied a desk in our office, I had never heard him shooting off his mouth on subjects about which he knew nothing.

When I got to our still empty office the following morning, I quickly cleared away the papers from my desk top so that I would have a large, flat surface on which to form pairs of bases held together by hydrogen bonds. Though I initially went back to my like-with-like prejudices, I saw all too well that they led nowhere. When Jerry came in I looked up, saw that it was not Francis, and began shifting the bases in and out of various other pairing possibilities. Suddenly I became aware that an adenine-thymine pair held together by two hydrogen bonds was identical in shape to a guanine-cytosine pair held together by at least two hydrogen bonds. All the hydrogen bonds seemed to form naturally; no fudging was required to make the two types of base pairs identical in shape. Quickly I called Jerry over to ask him whether this time he had any objection to my new base pairs.

I began shifting the bases in and out of several pairing possibilities

When he said no, my morale skyrocketed, for I suspected that we now had the answer to the riddle of why the number of purine residues exactly equaled the number of pyrimidine residues. Two irregular sequences of bases could be regularly packed in the center of a helix if a purine always hydrogen-bonded to a pyrimidine.

Upon his arrival Francis did not get more than halfway through the door before I let loose that the answer to everything was in our hands. Though as a matter of principle he maintained skepticism for a few moments, the similarly shaped A-T and G-C pairs had their expected impact. His quickly pushing the bases together in a number of different ways did not reveal any other way to satisfy Chargaff's rules. A few minutes later he spotted the fact that the two glycosidic bonds (joining base and sugar) of each base pair were systematically related by a diad axis perpendicular to the helical axis. Thus, both pairs could be flipflopped over and still have their glycosidic bonds facing in the same direction. This had the important consequence that a given chain could contain both purines and pyrimidines. At the same time, it strongly suggested that the backbones of the two chains must run in opposite directions.

At first glance, the answer to everything was in our hands

The question then became whether the A-T and G-C base pairs would easily fit the backbone configuration devised during the previous two weeks. At first glance this looked like a good bet, since I had left free in the center a large vacant area for the bases. However, we both knew that we would not be home until a complete model was built in which all the stereochemical contacts were satisfactory. There was also the obvious fact that the implications of its existence were far too important to risk crying wolf. Thus I felt slightly queasy when at lunch Francis winged into the Eagle to tell everyone within hearing distance that we had found the secret of life.

Francis' preoccupation with DNA quickly became full time. The first afternoon following the discovery that A-T and G-C base pairs had similar shapes, he went back to his thesis measurements, but his effort was ineffectual. Constantly he would pop up from his chair, worriedly look at the cardboard models, fiddle with other combinations, and then, the period of momentary uncertainty over, look satisfied and tell me how important our work was. I enjoyed Francis' words, even though they lacked the casual sense of understatement known to be the correct way to behave in Cambridge. It seemed almost unbelievable that the DNA structure was solved, that the answer was incredibly exciting, and that our names would be associated with the double helix as Pauling's was with the alpha helix.

It seemed almost unbelievable that the DNA structure was solved

When the Eagle opened at six, I went over with Francis to talk about what must be done in the next few days. Francis wanted no time lost in seeing whether a satisfactory three-dimensional model could be built, since the geneticists and nucleic-acid biochemists should not misuse their time and facilities any longer than necessary. They must be told the answer quickly, so that they could reorient their research upon our work. I was equally anxious to build the complete model. I thought more about Linus and the possibility that he might stumble upon the base pairs before we told him the answer.

That night, however, we could not firmly establish the double helix. Until the metal bases were on hand, any model building would be too sloppy to be convincing. I went back to Pop's to tell Elizabeth and Bertrand that Francis and I had probably beaten Pauling to the gate and that the answer would revolutionize biology. Both were genuinely pleased, Elizabeth with sisterly pride, Bertrand with the idea that he could report back to International Society that he had a friend who would win a Nobel Prize. Peter's reaction was equally enthusiastic and gave no indication that he minded the possibility of his father's first real scientific defeat.

I had probably beaten Pauling to the gate

The following morning I felt marvelously alive when I awoke. On my way to the Whim I slowly walked toward the Clare Bridge, staring up at the gothic pinnacles of the King's College Chapel that stood out sharply against the spring sky. I briefly stopped and looked over at the perfect Georgian features of the recently cleaned Gibbs Building, thinking that much of our success was due to the long uneventful periods when we walked among the colleges or unobtrusively read the new books that came into Heffer's Bookstore. After contentedly poring over *The Times,* I wandered into the lab to see Francis, unquestionably early, flipping the cardboard base pairs about an imaginary line. As far as a compass and ruler could tell him, both sets of base pairs neatly fitted into the backbone configuration. As the morning wore on, Max and John successively came by to see if we still thought we had it. Each got a quick, concise lecture from Francis, during the second of which I wandered down to see if the shop could be speeded up to produce the purines and pyrimidines later that afternoon.

Only a little encouragement was needed to get the final soldering accomplished in the next couple of hours. The brightly shining metal plates were then immediately used to make a model in which for the first time all the DNA components were present. In about an hour I had arranged the atoms in positions which satisfied both the x-ray data and the laws of stereochemistry. The resulting helix was right-handed with the two chains running in opposite directions. Only one person can easily play with a model, and so Francis did not try to check my work until I backed away and said that I thought everything fitted. While one interatomic contact was slightly shorter than optimal, it was not out of line with several published values, and I was not dis-

For the first time all the DNA components were present in the model

turbed. Another fifteen minutes' fiddling by Francis failed to find anything wrong, though for brief intervals my stomach felt uneasy when I saw him frowning. In each case he became satisfied and moved on to verify that another interatomic contact was reasonable. Everything thus looked very good when we went back to have supper with Odile.

Our dinner words fixed on how to let the big news out. Maurice, especially, must soon be told. But remembering the fiasco of sixteen months before, keeping King's in the dark made sense until exact coordinates had been obtained for all the atoms. It was all too easy to fudge a successful series of atomic contacts so that, while each looked almost acceptable, the whole collection was energetically impossible. We suspected that we had not made this error, but our judgment conceivably might be biased by the biological advantages of complementary DNA molecules. Thus the next several days were to be spent using a plumb line and a measuring stick to obtain the relative positions of all atoms in a single nucleotide. Because of the helical symmetry, the locations of the atoms in one nucleotide would automatically generate the other positions.

After coffee Odile wanted to know whether they would still have to go into exile in Brooklyn if our work was as sensational as everyone told her. Perhaps we should stay on in Cambridge to solve other problems of equal importance. I tried to reassure her, emphasizing that not all American men cut all their hair off and that there were scores of American women who did not wear short white socks on the streets. I had less success arguing that the States' greatest virtue was its wide-open spaces where people never went. Odile looked in horror at the prospect of being long without fashionably dressed people. Moreover, she could not believe that I was serious, since I had just had a tailor cut a tightly fitting blazer, unconnected with the sacks that Americans draped on their shoulders.

The next morning I again found that Francis had beaten me to the lab. He was already at work tightening the model on its support stands so that he could read off the atomic coordinates. While he moved the atoms back and forth, I sat on the top of my desk thinking about the form of the letters that I soon could write, saying that we had found something interesting. Occasionally, Francis would look disgusted when my daydreams kept me from observing that he needed my help to keep the model from collapsing as he rearranged the supporting ring stands.

Bragg had his first look late that morning. For several days he had been home with the flu and was in bed when he heard that Crick and I had thought up an ingenious DNA structure which might be important to biology. During his first free moment back in the Cavendish, he slipped away from his office for a direct view. Immediately he caught on to the complementary relation between the two chains and saw how an equivalence of adenine with thymine and guanine with cytosine was a logical consequence of the regular repeating shape of the sugar-phosphate backbone. As he was not aware of Chargaff's rules, I went over the experimental evidence on the relative proportions of the various bases, noticing that he was becoming increasingly excited by its potential implications for gene replication. When the question of the x-ray evidence came up, he saw why we had not yet called up the King's group. He was bothered, however, that we had not yet asked Todd's opinion. Telling Bragg that we had got the organic chemistry straight did not put him completely at ease. The chance that we were using

Bragg saw the complementary relation between the two chains

the wrong chemical formula admittedly was small, but, since Crick talked so fast, Bragg could never be sure that he would ever slow down long enough to get the right facts. So it was arranged that as soon as we had a set of atomic coordinates, we would have Todd come over.

Final refinements were finished the following evening

The final refinements of the coordinates were finished the following evening. Lacking the exact x-ray evidence, we were not confident that the configuration chosen was precisely correct. But this did not bother us, for we only wished to establish that at least one specific two-chain complementary helix was stereochemically possible. Until this was clear, the objection could be raised that, although our idea was aesthetically elegant, the shape of the sugar-phosphate backbone might not permit its existence. Happily, now we knew that this was not true, and so we had lunch, telling each other that a structure this pretty just had to exist.

With the tension now off, I went to play tennis with Bertrand, telling Francis that later in the afternoon I would write Luria and Delbrück about the double helix. It was so arranged that John Kendrew would call up Maurice to say that he should come out to see what Francis and I had just devised. Neither Francis nor I wanted the task. Earlier in the day the post had brought a note from Maurice to Francis, mentioning that he was now about to go full steam ahead on DNA and intended to place emphasis on model building.

Maurice needed but a minute's look at the model to like it

Maurice needed but a minute's look at the model to like it. He had been forewarned by John that it was a two-chain affair, held together by the A-T and G-C base pairs, and so immediately upon entering our office he studied its detailed features. That it had two, not three, chains did not bother him since he knew the evidence never seemed clear-cut. While

Maurice silently stared at the metal object, Francis stood by, sometimes talking very fast about what sort of x-ray diagram the structure should produce, then becoming strangely noiseless when he perceived that Maurice's wish was to look at the double helix, not to receive a lecture in crystallographic theory which he could work out by himself. There was no questioning of the decision to put guanine and thymine in the keto form. Doing otherwise would destroy the base pairs, and he accepted Jerry Donohue's spoken argument as if it were a commonplace.

The unforeseen dividend of having Jerry share an office with Francis, Peter, and me, though obvious to all, was not spoken about. If he had not been with us in Cambridge, I might still have been pumping for a like-with-like structure. Maurice, in a lab devoid of structural chemists, did not have anyone about to tell him that all the textbook pictures were wrong. But for Jerry, only Pauling would have been likely to make the right choice and stick by its consequences.

The next scientific step was to compare seriously the experimental x-ray data with the diffraction pattern predicted by our model. Maurice went back to London, saying that he would soon measure the critical reflections. There was not a hint of bitterness in his voice, and I felt quite relieved. Until the visit I had remained apprehensive that he would look gloomy, being unhappy that we had seized part of the glory that should have gone in full to him and his younger colleagues. But there was no trace of resentment on his face, and in his subdued way he was thoroughly excited that the structure would prove of great benefit to biology.

He was back in London only two days before he rang up to say that both he and Rosy found that their x-ray data strongly supported the double helix. They were quickly writing up their results and wanted to publish simultaneously with our announcement of the base pairs. *Nature* was a place for rapid publication, since if both Bragg and Randall strongly supported the manuscripts they might be published within a month of their receipt. However, there would not be only one paper from King's. Rosy and Gosling would report their results separately from Maurice and his collaborators.

X-ray data strongly supported the double helix

Rosy's instant acceptance of our model at first amazed me. I had feared that her sharp, stubborn mind, caught in her self-made antihelical trap, might dig up irrelevant results that would foster uncertainty about the correctness of the double helix. Nonetheless, like almost everyone else, she saw the appeal of the base pairs and accepted the fact that the structure was too pretty not to be true. Moreover, even before she learned of our proposal, the x-ray evidence had been forcing her more than she cared to admit toward a helical structure. The positioning of the backbone on the outside of the molecule was demanded by her evidence and, given the necessity to hydrogen-bond the bases together, the uniqueness of the A-T and G-C pairs was a fact she saw no reason to argue about.

At the same time, her fierce annoyance with Francis and me collapsed. Initially we were hesitant to discuss the double helix with her, fearing the testiness of our previous encounters. But Francis noticed her changed attitude when he was in London to talk with Maurice about details of the x-ray pictures. Thinking that Rosy wanted nothing to do with him, he spoke largely to Maurice, until he slowly perceived that Rosy wanted his crystallographic advice and was prepared to exchange unconcealed hostility for conversation between equals.

With obvious pleasure Rosy showed Francis her data, and for the first time he was able to see how foolproof was her assertion that the sugar-phosphate backbone was on the outside of the molecule. Her past uncompromising statements on this matter thus reflected first-rate science, not the outpourings of a misguided feminist.

Obviously affecting Rosy's transformation was her appreciation that our past hooting about model building represented a serious approach to science, not the easy resort of slackers who wanted to avoid the hard work necessitated by an honest scientific career. It also became apparent to us that Rosy's difficulties with Maurice and Randall were connected with her understandable need for being equal to the people she worked with. Soon after her entry into the King's lab, she had rebelled against its hierarchical character, taking offense because her first-rate crystallographic ability was not given formal recognition.

Two letters from Pasadena brought news that Pauling was still off base

Two letters from Pasadena that week brought the news that Pauling was still way off base. The first came from Delbrück, saying that Linus had just given a seminar during which he described a modification of his DNA structure. Most uncharacteristically, the manuscript he had sent to Cambridge had been published before his collaborator, R. B. Corey, could accurately measure the interatomic distances. When this was finally done, they found several unacceptable contacts that could not be overcome by minor jiggling. Pauling's model was thus also impossible on straightforward stereochemical grounds. He hoped, however, to save the situation by a modification suggested by his colleague Verner Schomaker. In the revised form the phosphate atoms were twisted 45 degrees, thereby allowing a different group of oxygen atoms to form a hydrogen bond. After Linus' talk, Delbrück told Schomaker he was not convinced that Linus was right, for he had just received my note saying that I had a new idea for the DNA structure.

Delbrück's comments were passed on immediately to Pauling, who quickly wrote off a letter to me. The first part betrayed nervousness – it did not come to the point, but conveyed an invitation to participate in a meeting on proteins to which he had decided to add a section on nucleic acids. Then he came out and asked for the details of the beautiful new structure I had written Delbrück about. Reading his letter, I drew a deep breath, for I realized that Delbrück did not know of the complementary double helix at the time of Linus' talk. Instead, he was referring to the like-with-like idea. Fortunately, by the time my letter reached Cal Tech the base pairs had fallen out. If they had not, I would have been in the dreadful position of having to inform Delbrück and Pauling that I had impetuously written of an idea which was only twelve hours old and lived only twenty-four before it was dead.

Todd made his official visit late in the week

Todd made his official visit late in the week, coming over from the chemical laboratory with several younger colleagues. Francis' quick verbal tour through the structure and its implications lost none of its zest for having been given several times each day for the past week. The pitch of his excitement was rising each day, and generally, whenever Jerry or I heard the voice of Francis shepherding in some new faces, we left our office until the new converts were let out and some traces of orderly work could resume. Todd was a different matter, for I wanted to hear him tell Bragg that we had correctly followed his advice on the chemistry of the sugar-phosphate backbone. Todd also went along with the keto configurations, saying that his organic-chemist friends had drawn enol groups for purely arbitrary reasons. Then he went off, after congratulating me and Francis for our excellent chemical work.

Soon I left Cambridge to spend a week in Paris. A trip to Paris to be with Boris and Harriet Ephrussi had been arranged some weeks earlier. Since the main part of our work seemed finished, I saw no reason to postpone a visit which now had the bonus of letting me be the first to tell Ephrussi's and Lwoff's labs about the double helix. Francis, however, was not happy, telling me that a week was far too long to abandon work of such extreme significance. A call for seriousness, however, was not to my liking – especially when John had just shown Francis and me a letter from Chargaff in which we were mentioned. A postscript asked for information on what his scientific clowns were up to.

Pauling first heard about the double helix from Delbrück. At the bottom of the letter that broke the news of the complementary chains, I had asked that he not tell Linus. I was still slightly afraid something would go wrong and did not want Pauling to think about hydrogen-bonded base pairs until we had a few more days to digest our position. My request, however, was ignored. Delbrück wanted to tell everyone in his lab and knew that within hours the gossip would travel from his lab in biology to their friends working under Linus. Also, Pauling had made him promise to let him know the minute he heard from me. Then there was the even more important consideration that Delbrück hated any form of secrecy in scientific matters and did not want to keep Pauling in suspense any longer.

Pauling's reaction was one of genuine thrill

Pauling's reaction was one of genuine thrill, as was Delbrück's. In almost any other situation, Pauling would have fought for the good points of his idea. The overwhelming biological merits of a self-complementary DNA molecule made him effectively concede the race. He did want, however, to see the evidence from King's before he considered the matter a closed book. This he hoped would be possible three weeks hence, when he would come to Brussels for a Solvay meeting on proteins in the second week of April.

In the next week the first drafts of our *Nature* paper got handed out and two were sent down to London for comments from Maurice and Rosy. They had no real objections except for wanting us to mention that Fraser in their lab had considered hydrogen-bonded bases prior to our work. His schemes, until then unknown to us in detail, always dealt with groups of three bases, hydrogen-bonded in the middle, many of which we now knew to be in the wrong tautomeric forms. Thus his idea did not seem worth resurrecting only to be quickly buried. However, when Maurice sounded upset at our objection, we added the necessary reference. Both Rosy's and Maurice's papers covered roughly the same ground and in each case interpreted their results in terms of the base pairs. For a while Francis wanted to expand our note to write at length about the biological implications. But finally he saw the point to a short remark and composed the sentence: "It has not escaped our notice that the specific pairing we have postulated immediately suggests a possible copying mechanism for the genetic material."

Sir Lawrence was shown the paper in its nearly final form

Sir Lawrence was shown the paper in its nearly final form. After suggesting a minor stylistic alteration, he enthusiastically expressed his willingness to post it to *Nature* with a strong covering letter. The solution to the structure was bringing genuine happiness to Bragg. That the result came out of the Cavendish and not Pasadena was obviously a factor. More important was the unexpectedly marvelous nature of the answer, and the fact that the x-ray method he had developed forty years before was at the heart of a profound insight into the nature of life itself.

The final version was ready to be typed on the last weekend of March. Our Cavendish typist was not on hand, and the brief job was given to my sister. There was no problem persuading her to spend a Saturday afternoon this way, for we told her that she was participating in perhaps the most famous event in biology since Darwin's book. Francis and I stood over her as she typed the nine-hundred-word article that began, "We wish to suggest a structure for the salt of deoxyribose nucleic acid (DNA). This structure has novel features which are of considerable biological interest." On Tuesday the manuscript was sent up to Bragg's office and on Wednesday, April 2, went off to the editors of *Nature*.

Perhaps the most famous event in biology since Darwin

Linus arrived in Cambridge on Friday night. On his way to Brussels for the Solvay meeting, he stopped off both to see Peter and to look at the model. Unthinkingly Peter arranged for him to stay at Pop's. Soon we found that he would have preferred a hotel. The presence of foreign girls at breakfast did not compensate for the lack of hot water in his room. Saturday morning Peter brought him into the office, where, after greeting Jerry with Cal Tech news, he set about examining the model. Though he still wanted to see the quantitative measurements of the King's lab, we supported our argument by showing him a copy of Rosy's original B photograph. All the right cards were in our hands and so, gracefully, he gave his opinion that we had the answer.

Elizabeth and I flew off the following afternoon to Paris, where Peter would join us the next day. Ten days hence she was sailing to the States on her way to Japan to marry an American she had known in college. These were to be our last days together, at least in the carefree spirit that had marked our escape from the Middle West and the American culture it was so easy to be ambivalent about. Monday morning we went over to the Faubourg St. Honoré for our last look at its elegance. There, peering in at a shop full of sleek umbrellas, I realized one should be her wedding present and we quickly had it. Afterwards she searched out a friend for tea while I walked back across the Seine to our hotel near the Palais du Luxembourg. Later that night with Peter we would celebrate my birthday. But now I was alone, looking at the long-haired girls near St. Germain des Prés and knowing they were not for me. I was twenty-five and too old to be unusual.

* * *

Epilogue

After two years of work Watson and Crick had a model of the structure of DNA. They had beat Pauling and Wilkins. Watson and Crick acknowledged that data supplied to them by Wilkins were very important to them. In 1962, when a Nobel Prize was awarded for determining the molecular structure of DNA, it was awarded to Watson, Crick, and Wilkins.

When Watson and Crick published their work in 1953, they opened the paper with the words, "We wish to suggest a structure for the salt of deoxyribose nucleic acid (DNA). This structure has novel features which are of considerable biological interest." The opening sentences of the paper proved to be one of the grandest understatements in the history of science.

The work of Watson and Crick stimulated an explosion in biology. It started a new science, molecular biology. Never before had so many scientists, all kinds of scientists, leaped to work on one problem. And never before had so much work been done so fast. Attention was now shifted from organisms and cells to the molecules which made up living things. Long-existing lines of division between physics, chemistry, and biology vanished as scientists all over the world went to work on DNA. What they would find would bring on another scientific revolution, perhaps the most significant scientific revolution in the history of man.

The beginning of another scientific revolution

Innovation & Achievement

1959

Jack St Clair Kilby

Robert N Noyce

11

They say we were lucky to invent the chip. Well, you can say it's luck hitting a home run with two out in the ninth in the final game of the World Series.

This chapter chronicles a thrilling adventure of the most powerful computer on earth: the human brain. It tells the story of two ingenious young Americans who hit upon a new idea that changed our daily life, spawned a multibillion-dollar global industry, and launched the "Second Industrial Revolution."

The story of two ingenious young Americans

This new idea is known to technicians as the "monolithic integrated circuit." To the rest of us it is the semiconductor chip, or microchip—the minute sliver of silicon at the heart of computers, calculators, digital clocks, and all the other wonders of our modern computer age.

The microchip was the brainchild of Jack Kilby and Robert Noyce, who changed the world as much as Thomas Edison, Alexander Graham Bell, and Henry Ford did. Yet they are virtually unknown to their fellow Americans. The narrative of their discovery is a scientific and enterpreneurial adventure story filled with suspense and surprises. It is a story of two quite different men—one, Kilby, a quiet, deliberate introvert who struggled through college, the other, Noyce, a razor-sharp, impulsive extrovert who has been a success at everything he has ever undertaken – and their race against other scientists around the world to find a solution to the "tyranny of numbers."

* * *

By the late 1950s the problem – the technical journals called it "the interconnections problem" or "the numbers barrier" or "the tyranny of numbers" – was a familiar one to the physicists and engineers who made up the electronics community. But the challenge was still a secret to the rest of the world at a time when the term "technological progress" had only positive connotations. Americans were looking ahead with happy anticipation to a near future when all the inventions of science fiction, from Dick Tracy's wrist radio to Buck Rogers's phone calls to Mars, would become facts of daily life. Already in 1958 a person could pull a transistor radio out of his pocket and hear news of a giant electronic computer that was decoding signals beamed at the speed of light from a miniaturized transmitter in a man-made satellite orbiting the earth at 18,000 miles per hour. Who could blame people for expecting new miracles tomorrow?

What accounted for this expectancy about the future of electronics? When, where, and how did it all start?

But first came the transistor

The seminal event that initiated the avalanche of innovations that constitute the solid-state electronics era occurred two days before Christmas of 1947 – the date of invention of the point-contact transistor – a transient type made obsolete four years later by the junction transistor. This first transistor was called point-contact because it used pointed wires in contact with a crystal of semiconductor and superficially resembled the "cat's whisker" crystal detectors of 1920 radios. Because it had no glass vacuum tube to break, no hot filament to burn out, it promised not only the elimination of all vacuum-tube bugs in computers in one fell swoop but much, much more. An early humanitarian example was the replacement of a massive hearing-aid vacuum-tube amplifier by one built into an eye-glass frame and, later, one concealable within the ear.

William Shockley and his team led the way

The point-contact inventors, Walter Brattain and John Bardeen, were members of a Bell Telephone Laboratories team headed by William Shockley. The goal had been prophesied in 1939 when Shockley wrote in his laboratory notebook that "an amplifier using semiconductors rather than vacuum is in principle possible." Metals are good conductors of electric current because they have approximately one current carrier, an electron, available for every atom. The semiconductors in transistors are, in effect, imperfect insulators and have vastly fewer carriers than a metal. The numbers of these few, but essential, carriers are controlled by the selection of foreign atoms introduced in manufacture and so are their charges, positive or negative. The first transistor semiconductor was the hitherto "useless" element germanium, with positive carriers produced by gallium and negative by arsenic. Silicon was an improvement – hence Silicon Valley. Different transistor types use different ways to amplify currents by altering the numbers of current carriers. Shockley's 1939 idea was to do so by penetrating the semiconductor with an electric field. He returned to this idea in 1945 when wartime activities ceased.

Shockley's field-effect idea was a pre- and postwar failure – but a creative one. It was a mystery for current science. While seeking new science to solve this mystery, Bardeen and Brattain created experiments and theories, observed the "transistor effect," and invented the point-contact transistor. In seeking a deeper understanding of the point-contact transistor, with its junctions between metal points and the semiconductor, Shockley invented the junction transistor. In the junction transistor the junction is what electrically joins two regions of a crystal, one region having positive carriers and the other negative. Technological advances have led to families of transistors using improvements of the 1939 field-effect principle.

A Nobel Prize in Physics

For their contributions to transistor science, William Shockley, John Bardeen, and Walter H. Brattain shared the 1956 Nobel Prize in Physics.

Following this, there was then the tecnetron, the spacistor, the nuvistor, the thyristor. It hardly seemed remarkable when the venerable British journal *New Scientist* predicted the imminent development of a new device, the "neuristor," which would perform all the functions of the human neuron and so make possible the ultimate prosthetic device – the artificial brain. Late in 1956 a *Life* magazine reporter dug out a secret Pentagon plan for a new troop-carrying missile that could pick up a platoon at a base in the United States, "loop through outer space, and land the troops 500 miles behind enemy lines in less than 30 minutes." A computer in the missile's nose cone would assure the pinpoint accuracy required to make such flights possible. A computer in a nose cone? The computers of the 1950s were enormous contraptions that filled whole rooms – in some cases, whole buildings – and consumed the power of a locomotive. But that, too, would give way to progress. Sperry-Rand, the makers of UNIVAC, the computer that had leapt to overnight fame on November 4, 1952, when it predicted Eisenhower's electoral victory one hour after the polls closed, was said to be working on computers that would fit on a desk top. And that would be just the beginning. Soon enough there would be computers in a briefcase, computers in a wristwatch, computers on the head of a pin.

The people in the electronics business who were supposed to make these miracles come true read the articles with a rueful sense of amusement. There were plans on paper to implement just about every fantasy the popular press reported; there were, indeed, preliminary blueprints that went far beyond the popular imagination. But it was all on paper, impossible to produce because of the limitation posed by the tyranny of numbers. The advent of the transistor offered enormous, world-shaking possibilities—but they would never be realized unless somebody found a way around the problem of numbers. The interconnections problem stood as an impassable barrier blocking all future progress in electronics.

The successful invention—The Monolithic Idea—resolved the tyranny of numbers by reducing the numbers to one: a complete circuit would consist of one part—a single ("monolithic") block of semiconductor material containing all the components and all the interconnections of the most complex circuit designs. The tangible product of that idea, known to the engineers as the monolithic integrated circuit and to the world at large as the semiconductor chip, has changed the world as fundamentally as did the telephone, the light bulb, the horseless carriage. The integrated circuit is the heart of clocks, computers, cameras, and calculators, of Pac-Man and pacemakers, of deep-space probes and deep-sea sensors, of toasters, typewriters, and data transmission networks. The National Academy of Sciences has declared the integrated circuit the progenitor of the

The progenitor of the Second Industrial Revolution

"Second Industrial Revolution." The first Industrial Revolution enhanced man's physical prowess and freed people from the drudgery of back-breaking manual labor; the revolution spawned by the chip enhances our intellectual prowess and frees people from the drudgery of mind-numbing computational labor. British physicist Sir Ieuan Madlock, formerly Her Majesty's chief science advisor, called the integrated circuit "the most remarkable technology ever to hit mankind." California businessman Jerry Sanders, founder of Advanced Micro Devices, Inc., offered a more pointed assessment: "Integrated circuits are the crude oil of the eighties."

All this came about because two young Americans came up with a new idea – or, more precisely, a not-so-new idea. In fact, the principle underlying the semiconductor revolution was one of the oldest ideas in electronics.

The idea occurred to Jack Kilby at the height of summer, when everyone else was on vacation and he had the lab to himself.

Texas Instruments then had a mass vacation policy; everybody took off the same few weeks in July. Kilby, who hadn't been around long enough to earn vacation time, was left alone in the semiconductor lab. He was, "discouraged," he wrote later, "I felt it likely that I would be put to work on a proposal for the Micro Module program when vacation was over unless I came up with a good idea very quickly."

Kilby plunged in with his wide-angle approach, soaking up every fact he could about the problem at hand, and the ways Texas Instruments might solve it. Among much else, he took a close, analytical look at his new firm and its operations. The obvious fact that emerged was Texas Instruments' heavy commitment to silicon. To capitalize on its victory in the race to develop silicon transistors, T.I. had invested millions of dollars in equipment and techniques to purify silicon and manufacture transistors with it. "If Texas Instruments was going to do something," Kilby explained later, "it probably had to involve silicon."

This conclusion provided Kilby the focus he needed for the narrow, concentrated phase of problem solving. He began to think, and think hard, about silicon. What could you do with silicon?

An idea of cosmic dimensions

Jack Kilby's answer to that question has come to be known as The Monolithic Idea. It was an idea, as events would prove, of literally cosmic dimensions, an idea that would change the daily life of the world and be honored in the textbooks with a name of its own. But at the time—it was July of 1958—Kilby only hoped that his boss would let him build a model and give the new idea a try.

The boss was still an unknown quantity. It had been less than two months since Jack Kilby had arrived in Dallas to begin work at Texas Instruments, and the new employee still did not have a firm sense of where he stood. Kilby had been delighted and flattered when Willis Adcock, the famous silicon pioneer, had offered him a job in T.I.'s semiconductor research group, but the pleasure was tempered with some misgivings. Jack's wife, Barbara, and his two young daughters had been happy in Milwaukee. For that matter, Jack had prospered there. He had spent ten years in Milwaukee at a small electronics firm called Centralab. During that decade, Kilby made twelve patentable inventions (including the reduced titanate capacitor and the steatite-packaged transistor) and one important discovery. He discovered the sheer joy of inventing. It was problem solving, really: you identified the problem, worked through 5 or 50 or 500 possible approaches, found ways to circumvent the limits that nature had built into materials and forces, and perfected the one solution that worked. It was an intense, creative process, and Jack fell in love with it. It was that infatuation with problem solving that had lured him, at the age of thirty-four, to take a chance on a new job in Dallas. Texas Instruments was putting him to work on the most important problem in electronics.

Right from the start he thought he might be on to something revolutionary

And now, on a muggy summer's day in Dallas, Jack Kilby had an idea that might break down the barrier. Right from the start, he thought he might be on to something revolutionary, but he did his best to retain a professional caution; a lot of revolutionary ideas, after all, turn out to have fatal flaws. Day after day, working alone in the empty lab, he went over the idea, scratching pictures in his lab notebook, sketching circuits, planning a model; the more he studied the idea, the better it looked. When his colleagues came back from vacation, Jack showed his notebook to Willis Adcock. "He was enthused, but skeptical," Kilby wrote later. "I was very interested," Adcock recalled afterward. "But... what Jack was saying, it was pretty damn cumbersome; you would have had a terrible time trying to produce it." A test would require a model; that could cost $10,000, maybe more. There were other projects around, and Adcock was supposed to move ahead on them.

Jack Kilby is a gentle soul, easygoing and unhurried. A lanky, casual, down-home type with a big leathery face that wraps around an enormous smile, he talks slowly, in a quiet voice that has never lost the soft country twang of Great Bend, Kansas, where he grew up; that deliberate mode of speech reflects a careful, deliberate way of thinking. Adcock, in contrast, is a zesty sprite who talks a mile a minute and still can't keep up with his racing train of thought.

That summer, though, it was Kilby who was pushing to race ahead. After all, if they didn't develop the idea, somebody else might hit on it. T.I. was hardly the only place in the world where people were trying to overcome the tyranny of numbers.

On July 24, 1958, Kilby, in his lab notebook, wrote down The Monolithic Idea: "The following circuit elements could be made on a single slice: resistors, capacitor, distributed capacitor, transistor." He made rough sketches of how each of the components could be realized by proper arrangements of N-type and P-type semiconductor material.

On September 12, 1958, Jack Kilby's oscillator-on-a-chip, half an inch long and narrower than a toothpick, was finally ready. A group of T.I. executives gathered in Kilby's area in the lab to see if this tiny and wholly new species of circuit would really work. Conceptually, of course, Kilby knew it would; he had thought the thing through so often, there couldn't be a flaw. Or could there? After all, nobody had ever done anything like this before. Kilby was strangely nervous as he hooked up the wires from the battery to his small monolithic circuit, and from the circuit to the oscilloscope. He fiddled with the dials on the oscilloscope. He checked the connections. He looked up at Adcock, who gave him a here goes nothin' shrug. He checked the connections again. He took a deep breath. He pushed the switch. Immediately a bright green snake of light started undulating across the screen in a perfect, unending sine wave. The integrated circuit, the answer to the tyranny of numbers, had worked. The men in the room looked at the sine wave, looked at Kilby, looked at the chip, looked at the sine wave again. Then everybody broke into broad smiles. A new era in electronics had been born.

He took a deep breath and pushed the switch

* * *

The Robert Noyce Story

The Monolithic Idea occurred to Robert Noyce in the depth of winter – or at least in the mildly chilly season that passes for winter in the sunny valley south of San Francisco Bay that is known today because of the idea, as "Silicon Valley." Unlike Kilby, Bob Noyce did not have to check with the boss when he got an idea; at thirty-one, Noyce was the boss.

It was January 1959, and the valley was still largely an agricultural domain, with only a handful of electronics firms intruding on the peach and prune orchards. One of those pioneering firms, Fairchild Semiconductor, had been started late in 1957 by a group of physicists and engineers who guessed – correctly, as it turned out – that they could become rich by producing improved versions of transistors and other microelectronic devices. The group was long on technical talent and short on managerial skills, but one of the founders turned out to have both – Bob Noyce. A slender, square-jawed man who exudes the easy self-assurance of a jet pilot, Noyce has an unbounded curiosity that has led him to take up, at one time or another, hobbies ranging from singing madrigals to flying seaplanes. His doctorate was in physics, and his technical specialty was solid state electronics; at Fairchild, though, he later became fascinated with the discipline of management, and he gravitated to the position of director of research and development. In that job Noyce spent a lot of time searching for profitable solutions to the problems facing the electronics industry; he thought about the optimum alloy to use for base and emitter contacts in double-diffuse transistors, about efficient ways to passivate junctions within a silicon wafer. And he also gave some thought, in the winter of 1958-59, to the tyranny of numbers.

Unlike the quiet Kilby, who does his best work alone, thinking carefully through a problem, Noyce is an outgoing, loquacious, impulsive inventor who needs somebody to listen to his ideas and point out the ones that couldn't possibly work. That winter Noyce's sounding board was his friend Gordon Moore, a thoughtful, cautious physical chemist who was another cofounder of Fairchild Semiconductor. "I spent a lot of time explaining to Gordon on the blackboard how you might do some of these things," Noyce recalled later.

Not suddenly, but gradually, in the first weeks of 1959, Noyce worked out the idea; on January 23, he remembers, "all the bits and pieces came together." He grabbed his lab notebook and wrote down The Monolithic Idea, in words quite similar to those Jack Kilby had entered in his notebook six months before: ". . . it would be desirable to make multiple devices on a single piece of silicon, in order to be able to make interconnections between devices as part of the manufacturing process, and thus reduce size, weight, etc. as well as cost per active element."

Like Kilby, Noyce felt fairly sure from the beginning that he was onto something important. "There was a tremendous motivation then to do something about the numbers barrier," he recalled later. "The (electronics) industry was in a situation – for example, in a computer with tens of thousands of components, tens of thousands of interconnections – where things were just impossibly expensive to make. And this looked like a way to deal with that.... I can remember telling Gordon one day that we might have here a solution to a real big problem." Off and on, all through 1957 and 1958, Noyce thought about the interconnections problem. In retrospect, he can see now, The Monolithic Idea should have come to him much earlier. "Here we were in a factory that was making all these transistors in a perfect array on a single wafer," Noyce says,

Needed: a solution to a real big problem

"and then we cut them apart into tiny pieces and had to hire thousands of women with tweezers to pick them up and try to wire them together. It just seemed so stupid. It's expensive, it's unreliable, it clearly limits the complexity of the circuits you can build. It was an acute problem. The answer, of course, was don't cut them apart in the first place – but nobody realized that then." Instead, Noyce was stuck in a rut. He worked on standard ideas for making circuit components in smaller sizes and higher performance. That work crowded out thoughts about the tyranny of numbers.

The enemy: a piece of dust

It was concern about another problem which brought Noyce to The Monolithic Idea. Double-diffusion transistors – the tiny three-layer chips of N-P-N silicon – were highly susceptible to contamination. A piece of dust, a stray electric charge, a minute whiff of contaminating gas would break down the P-N junctions and impair transistor action. One day in 1958, Jean Hoerni came to Noyce with a theoretical solution: he would place a layer of silicon oxide on top of the N-P-N chip, like icing atop the three-layer cake. The oxide would hold fast to the silicon and protect it from contaminants.

"It's building a transistor inside a cocoon of silicon dioxide," Noyce explains, "so that it never gets contaminated. It's like setting up your jungle operating room. You put the patient inside a plastic bag and you operate inside of that, and you don't have all the flies of the jungle sitting on the wound." Noyce quickly called in the firm's patent lawyer to put together a patent application. Sensing that this idea might have other applications in electronics, the lawyer wanted to write the application in the broadest language. He told Noyce that the application should be made as expansive as possible. Every time they talked about it, the lawyer would pose a challenge: "What else can you do with this idea?"

Looking back today, Noyce can see clearly that it was the lawyer's question that pushed him out of his mental rut and provoked the leap of insight that became The Monolithic Idea. What else? What else could you do? Couldn't you, in fact, build a complete circuit, an *integrated* circuit, all on a single chip of silicon? Wouldn't that overcome the tyranny of numbers?

The lawyer's question pushed him out of his mental rut

"I don't remember any time when a light bulb went off and the whole thing was there," Noyce says. "It was more like, every day, you would say, well, if I could do this, then maybe I could do that, and that would let me do this, and eventually you had the concept."

On January 23, 1959, "all the bits and pieces came together," and Noyce filled four pages of his lab notebook with a remarkably complete description of an integrated circuit. "In many applications," he wrote, "it would be desirable to make multiple devices on a single piece of silicon, in order to be able to make interconnections between devices as part of the manufacturing process, and thus reduce size, weight, etc. as well as cost per active element." Noyce went on to explain how resistors and capacitors could be fabricated on a silicon chip, and how the whole monolithic circuit could be connected by metal contacts printed right onto the chip. He also set forth a rough sketch of a computer circuit – a circuit that would add two numbers – realized in integrated form. Six months after Jack Kilby had reached the same destination, Bob Noyce had arrived at The Monolithic Idea.

On January 23, all the bits and pieces came together

* * *

News travels quickly in the electronics industry. By the spring of 1959 there were rumors about a major new development at Texas Instruments. Nobody knew exactly what T.I. had done, but it was not impossible to guess which problem this breakthrough was designed to solve. Noyce again called in the lawyer to prepare a patent application for a new idea—"a unitary circuit structure . . . to facilitate the inclusion of numerous semiconductor devices within a single body of material." This time, it was decided to write a detailed, precise patent application, a document that could serve as a shield. This strategic decision would become the decisive factor in a bitter ten-year legal battle fought all the way to the United States Supreme Court.

The scientific community, meanwhile, agreed to agree that Kilby and Noyce deserved joint credit for The Monolithic Idea. The two men were both awarded the National Medal of Science for overcoming the tyranny of numbers, and both were inducted into the National Inventors' Hall of Fame. Today, Kilby is generous in describing Noyce's work on the invention, and Noyce is equally generous about Kilby. In the textbooks, Kilby gets credit for the idea of integrating components on a chip, and Noyce for working out a practical way to connect those components. Among their fellow engineers, Kilby and Noyce are referred to as "co-inventors" of the chip, a term that both men find satisfactory.

The integrated circuit was an enormous success

The integrated circuit was an enormous success because it solved an enormously important problem—the tyranny of numbers. But the success story was also a matter of timing. The chip came along just when the computer was growing up, and chips turned out to be the perfect tools for the digital math and logic that computers use. "The synergy between a new component and a new application generated an explosive growth for both," Bob Noyce wrote in a retrospective article two decades after The Monolithic Idea was born: "The computer was the ideal market . . . a much larger market than could have been provided by the traditional applications of electronics in communications."

In traditional circuitry, involving discrete components wired together, resistors and capacitors were cheap, but switching components such as vacuum tubes and transistors were relatively expensive. This situation was nicely suited to the manufacture of radios, television sets, and the like; an ordinary table radio of the 1950s used two or three dozen capacitors and resistors but only two or three transistors. With integrated circuits, the traditional economies were reversed. Resistors and capacitors, which use up power and take up a lot of room on a chip, became expensive; transistors were compact, simple to make, and cheap. That situation is precisely suited for computers and other digital devices, which need large numbers of switches – transistors – and small quantities of other components.

Innovation & Achievement

Thoughts on Innovation & Achievement

In facing the creative task of conceiving and executing a new Westvaco volume each year, one tends to try very hard to keep in a perpetual state of creative readiness. And, it might be said that the time spent in libraries and used bookstores is directly proportional to the length of the list of possible subjects for consideration. This year, although the creative possibilities were many, one idea–the idea of *Innovation & Achievement*–seemed to rise above all of the others fairly early in the creative process. It seemed to be the most appropriate and timely.

In hindsight, inspiration came from several quarters. Surely, we were influenced by the fundamental business philosophy of our company. Throughout Westvaco, we are working very hard to build strengths which are truly unique in our field. Innovation has become a thoroughly engrained way of life and, as such, it represents not only a major competitive strength for today, but also bodes well for the future.

We were also inspired by the many conversations we were privileged to have over the past several years on the subject with members of the senior management of the company who encouraged us to undertake the challenge of producing the work. They also participated actively, providing ideas and inspiration.

In thinking about innovation and the influence it has had on each of us, one only has to review one's own personal experience of growing up in America. For each of us our first exposure to the marvels of American innovation might be different, but surely the excitement of change can easily be remembered. From the horse and buggy to the automobile, from Kitty Hawk to the moon, Americans alive today have been participants as well as observers in new milestones of achievement on new frontiers of science and technology.

In organizing our thoughts on the subject, we were also mindful of the experience of history. We recalled the dire prediction of the British economist, Thomas Malthus. In 1798, Malthus predicted that, because of what he projected as being an imbalance between population growth and food supply, the world would certainly face starvation. Yet, in thinking about Malthus, it occurred to us that history was once again able to demonstrate the extraordinary power of the creative individual. Malthus underestimated by a wide margin the creativity and commitment of the marvelous people who invented the reapers, the threshers, the combines, and the tractors, as well as the impact of fertilizer and the quantum increase in productivity that resulted in such an abundance in food supply.

Another example of more recent vintage occurred during World War II when, early in the conflict, our country was denied nearly all of its natural rubber supply. The doomsayers predicted dire consequences, but, once again, in a society which encourages individual creative effort, the problem was solved. Synthetic rubber replaced the need for natural rubber. The crisis ended. A new industry found its niche. And the nation prevailed in a time of great crisis.

In producing *Innovation & Achievement* as in any creative endeavor, we traveled many other roads to reach our final destination. As part of the search for outstanding content, we discussed the subject with a number of other thoughtful and helpful people very close to the subject at hand. We had interesting and helpful conversations with biographers, authors, and several of the scientists themselves.

We outlined our task to the people at Bell Laboratories who gave us access to information on Robert Noyce and Jack Kilby. We had numerous talks with Dr. William Shockley who helped immensely by taking the time to write several descriptive paragraphs authenticating the importance of the transistor as the basis for other monumental breakthroughs that followed. We were also in touch with the Henry Ford Museum and the Inventors Hall of Fame. And we had the thrill of spending an hour with Nobel Laureate, James Watson, hearing first hand the nature of his midwestern upbringing, the competition for an incredibly important breakthrough and the achievement of what many believe to be the most significant biological discovery since Darwin.

Facing the creative challenge of actually crafting the book caused us to become acutely sensitive to, in all probability experiencing ourselves, some of the same emotions which were undoubtedly experienced by those whose achievements we have tried to bring to life on these pages. These are feelings we have experienced a number of times before. Yet, regardless of how many times we've been there, the moment of topping off a project such as this one is always exciting. It's memorable. It's a creative happening. It's worth savoring.

You begin with a blank piece of paper and an idea. You struggle long and hard for the right title. You travel far and wide to find good source material. You edit and then you edit again. You develop a design concept for the cover, spine, text, endleaves, chapter breaks, colophon, slipcase, mailing carton, ex libris card, and shipping label. You select the typography. You set the type. You order the stamping dies. You spend endless hours proofreading. You prepare the mechanical artwork from which the printer can make his printing plates. You write the foreword. You order the fine paper, the material for the cover, and the ribbon for the bookmark.

Everyone gives a lot. You've been a stickler for the little things that make a difference. So much care is taken. And now is the time for reckoning. Needless to say, it's one thing getting ready for a new book, crafting the words, thinking about the graphics, trying to envision how the volume will actually look, handling a hundred and one details, striving to do your very best. But it's something else to be there, with the printer, precisely at the moment of truth, seeing everything come together.

The presses hum with electronic precision, doing wonderful things to the sheets of fine white paper. The pungent odor of ink strains the senses. The hands of robots gingerly move each sheet of paper out of the way while master printers peer through magnified scopes to assure perfection. Coming off the press, the sheets begin to achieve a new dimension. They grow like a rising tide on the wooden skids. The skids attain the look of cubes of white marble. The tops are colorfully adorned with the images you created.

The bindery is a beehive. You can hear the buzzing of machines. The machines are stitching the bindings for the books. The trimming blades flash like sabers in a field of fusileers.

The books march down the conveyor. The parade seems endless. You pick up one of the books. Yes, it's as you imagined it would be, maybe even a little nicer. It's your baby. But not for long. You place the book back on the moving belt. It disappears over the horizon with a hundred others. The books are sealed in a large box for a predestined journey. It's like seeing your child leave home for the first time.

Suddenly, the emotions change. The pressure is off for a while. It's time to honor the wisdom of a contemporary philosopher: "Don't forget to smell the roses." It's what writers and graphic designers live for. A warm glow of satisfaction begins to overcome the letdown of saying goodbye to a part of your life.

But there's an awful lot to be thankful for, too. You've had a wonderful opportunity to put whatever talents you have to work. You've helped create something of value. You've watched your book grow and mature. You've enjoyed the give and take of competing ideas. And, so, the thought does cross your mind: Maybe the part of your life that you're saying goodbye to is a part that will really endure.

Speaking of things that will endure, we discovered in preparing the volume a number of profound statements which relate to our subject but which are really too valuable to discard even though we've put the book to bed. They are the many quotations and other gems of wisdom which we are including as the finale to *Innovation & Achievement*. We hope you will find them as inspirational as we did.

Alexis de Tocqueville Of all the countries in the world, America is that in which the spread of ideas and of human industry is most continual and most rapid. I know that this intense industrial and intellectual movement is particularly encouraged by education, by the sort of government America enjoys, and by the altogether special situation in which the Americans find themselves.

Charles Proteus Steinmetz If I were to bequeath to every young person one virtue, I would give him or her the spirit of divine discontent, for without it the world would stand still.

Ralph Waldo Emerson Ideas must work through the brains and the arms of good and brave men, or they are no better than dreams.

John Burroughs For anything worth having one must pay the price; and the price is always work, patience, love, self-sacrifice—no paper currency, no promises to pay, but the gold of real service.

Charles F. Kettering Great steps in human progress are made by things that don't work the way philosophy thought they should. If things always worked the way they should, you could write the history of the world from now on. But they don't and it is these deviations from the normal that make human progress.

Alfred P. Sloan, Jr. Growth and progress are related, for there is no resting place for an enterprise in a competitive economy. Obstacles, conflicts, new problems in various shapes, and new horizons arise to stir the imagination and continue the progress of industry.

George Gilder The future is forever incalculable; only in freedom can its challenges be mastered.

Let those who seek a perpetual safe harbor continue to do so. Let them renounce risk for themselves, if they choose. What no one has a right to do is renounce it for all the rest of us, or to pursue the chimerical goal of a risk-free society for some by eliminating the rewards of risk for everyone.

Walter B. Wriston

Every revolution was first a thought in one man's mind and when the same thought occurs to another man, it is the key to that era.

Ralph Waldo Emerson

If nature has made any one thing less susceptible than all others of exclusive property, it is the action of the thinking power called an idea, which an individual may exclusively possess as long as he keeps it to himself; but the moment it is divulged, it forces itself into the possession of every one, and the receiver cannot dispossess himself of it.

Thomas Jefferson

The inventions in mechanic arts, the discoveries in natural philosophy, navigation, and commerce, and the advancement of civilization and humanity, have occasioned changes in the condition of the world and the human character which would have astonished the most refined nations of antiquity.

John Adams

The ultimate good desired is better reached by free trade in ideas — the best test of truth is the power of the thought to get itself accepted in the competition of the market.

Oliver Wendell Holmes

Innovation is the design and development of something new, as yet unknown and not in existence, which will establish a new economic configuration out of the old, known, existing elements.

Peter Drucker

The power of imagination makes us infinite.

John Muir

Alfred P. Sloan, Jr. The perpetuation of an unusual success or the maintenance of an unusually high standard of leadership in any industry is sometimes more difficult than the attainment of that success or leadership in the first place.

Thomas A. Edison Be as brave as your fathers before you. Have faith! Go forward.

Charles F. Kettering We work day after day, not to finish things, but to make the future better... because we will spend the rest of our lives there.

Thomas Jefferson It is impossible for a man who takes a survey of what is already known, not to see what an immensity in every branch of science yet remains to be discovered. I join you, therefore, in branding as cowardly the idea that the human mind is incapable of further advances.

John W. Gardner Life never was a series of easy victories. We can't win every round or arrive at a neat solution to every problem. But driving, creative effort to solve problems is the breath of life, for a civilization or an individual.

Sir Francis Darwin The credit goes to the man that convinces the world, not to the man to whom the idea first occurs.

Michelangelo The idea is there, locked inside, all you have to do is remove the excess stone.

John Greenleaf Whittier Let the thick curtain fall, I know better than all, how little I have gained, how vast the unattained.

Ralph Waldo Emerson There is so much to be done that we ought to begin quickly to bestir ourselves.

If one advances confidently in the direction of his dreams, and endeavors to live the life which he has imagined, he will meet with a success unexpected in common hours.

Henry D. Thoreau

In the United States, boldness of enterprise is the foremost cause of its rapid progress, its strength, and its greatness.

Alexis de Tocqueville

The person hard to satisfy moves forward. The person satisfied with what he or she has done moves backwards.

Charles Proteus Steinmetz

New discoveries in science... will continue to create a thousand new frontiers for those who will still adventure.

Herbert Hoover

We have spent the prime of our lives in procuring the precious blessing of liberty. Let them spend theirs in showing that it is the great parent of science and of virtue; and that a nation will be great in both, always in proportion as it is free.

Thomas Jefferson

It is almost impossible to exaggerate the importance to general welfare of the willingness of individuals to take a personal risk. The worst thing that can happen to a society, as to an individual, is to become terrified of uncertainty.

Walter B. Wriston

Individual liberty is individual power, and as the power of a community is a mass compounded of individual powers, the nation which enjoys the most freedom must necessarily be in proportion to its numbers the most powerful nation.

John Adams

The empires of the future are the empires of the mind.

Winston Churchill

Edward Schon The new idea either finds a champion or dies... No ordinary involvement with a new idea provides the energy required to cope with the indifference and resistance that major technological change provokes... Champions of new inventions display persistence and courage of heroic quality.

Ralph Waldo Emerson Nature arms each man with some faculty which enables him to do easily some feat impossible to any other.

James Russell Lowell If the works of the great poets teach anything, it is to hold mere inventions somewhat cheap. It is not the finding of a thing, but the making of something out of it after it is found, that is of consequence.

Everett Hale I am only one, but I am one. I cannot do everything, but I can do something. What I can do, I should do and, with the help of God, I will do!

Theodore Roosevelt Far better it is to dare mighty things, to win glorious triumphs, even though checkered by failure, than to take rank with those poor spirits who neither enjoy much nor suffer much, because they live in the gray twilight that knows not victory nor defeat.

Nikola Tesla I do not think there is any thrill that can go through the human heart like that felt by the inventor as he sees some creation of the brain unfolding to success... Such emotions make a man forget food, sleep, friends, love, everything.

Thomas J. Watson Today's pioneers are building tomorrow's progress.

Henry D. Thoreau Man's capacities have never been measured, nor are we to judge of what we can do by any precedents, so little has been tried.

About the design

Each volume in the Westvaco library of limited editions has been carefully crafted to reflect a unique visual image. For the 1987 volume, we wanted to achieve a functional design; therefore, our emphasis on simplicity.

As a primary element, we decided to employ the use of an early flag from our nation's history, the classic thirteen stars, representing a new constellation, positioned alongside the alternating stripes. Each of the stars represents one of the thirteen American innovators whose accomplishments we have documented. The designer then placed the entire flag motif on the endleaves and the circle of stars singly on the slipcase.

Because creativity is, by nature, an intuitive process involving the thought process of an individual, we decided also to use the great strength of a person's true mark of individualism, the handwritten signature. Together they form the primary visual element on the frontispiece and then are used individually on each division page.

While the formation of thoughts and ideas appears to have considerable fluidity as they are contemplated, we felt that the design should reflect a certain discipline which is always needed for an idea to be brought to fruition. This thought resulted in our use of the grid pattern which has been traditionally used by scientists and engineers as their basic pallet for ideation.

The headlines for each chapter are crafted to reflect, whenever possible, a precise moment in time when the creative breakthrough occurred. The sidebars, which appear in a second color, are set in italics to create the feeling of handwritten notes in the margin of a diary or log book.

Acknowledgments

Various chapter selections
from *American Science and Invention*, by Mitchell Wilson,
copyright 1954, renewed 1982 by Stella Adler,
Victoria Wilson, and Erica Spellman.

Chapter 1
Reprinted with permission of
Macmillan Publishing Company
from *The World of Eli Whitney*
by Jeannette Mirsky and Allan Nevins.
Copyright 1952 by Jeannette Mirsky
and Allan Nevins and renewed 1980.

Chapter 2
From the book, *Robert Fulton*, by Cynthia Owen Philip.
Copyright 1985 by Cynthia Owen Philip.
Reprinted with permission of
the publisher, Franklin Watts, Inc.

Chapters 6 and 7
Selections from *Fire of Genius* by Ernest V. Heyn.
Copyright 1976 by Ernest V. Heyn.
Reprinted by permission of Doubleday & Company, Inc.

Chapter 9
Selections from
The Public Image of Henry Ford by David L. Lewis.
Copyright 1976 by Wayne State University Press.
Reprinted with the permission
of the publisher.

Excerpts from *My Life & Work* by Henry Ford.
Copyright 1922 by Doubleday & Company, Inc.
Reprinted with the permission
of the publisher.

Colophon

This limited edition of
Innovation & Achievement
is produced solely by Westvaco people.

The foreword and selections are by John C. Callihan.

The design of the book is by Karen M. Bloom.

Production coordinator: Jean C. Cunningham.
Special assistance: Dawn Burke, Phyllis Freed,
Paula Gilligan, C. Margaret Lapnow,
and Alexandra Lehmann.

The phototype is Baskerville,
with Sabon italic,
set by Finn Typographic.
Offset printing is by Meriden-Stinehour Press
on Clear Spring® Offset Vellum
made by Westvaco at its
fine papers mill in Wickliffe, Kentucky.
Binding is by Zahrndt, Inc.

Studio assistance: Anagraphics, Inc.